BOWVAYNE

MYTH BUSTERS

REAL-LIFE ADVENTURES IN THE WORLD OF THE SUPERNATURAL

PUFFIN BOOKS

PUFFIN BOOKS

Published by the Penguin Group
Penguin Books Ltd, 27 Wrights Lane, London W8 5TZ, England
Penguin Books USA Inc., 375 Hudson Street, New York, New York 10014, USA
Penguin Books Australia Ltd, Ringwood, Victoria, Australia
Penguin Books Canada Ltd, 10 Alcorn Avenue, Toronto, Ontario, Canada M4V 3B2
Penguin Books (NZ) Ltd, 182–190 Wairau Road, Auckland 10, New Zealand

Penguin Books Ltd, Registered Offices: Harmondsworth, Middlesex, England

First published 1996
1 3 5 7 9 10 8 6 4 2

Copyright © Bowvayne, 1996
Illustrations copyright © Douglas Carrel, 1996
Maps copyright © Stephen Player, 1996
All rights reserved

The moral right of the author has been asserted

Filmset in Monotype Palatino

Made and printed in England by Clays Ltd, St Ives plc

Dedication

Andy 'Get Stuffed' Barber for becoming the latest to join our exclusive club. The fantastically unique 'Let there never be another!' Norman Bradley for believing in Mythbusters. Mattie Deal for 'blubbering uncontrollably' every time we've seen something slightly mysterious. Ian Digweed for stalling cars beyond the call of duty. Elizabeth for word-processing 'Clapham Wood' in the presence of a tiptoeing madman in underpants whose only word was 'Prizes!' Glynda Gabriel for wanting to see me in a court jester's outfit. Beth Macdougall: patient, understanding, fun, in fact for everything. (When do I get to meet your pet banana lounger?) Marion for braving the 'weird wood' with us in '88. Ruth for saving the day. Editor and honorary Mythbuster Richard Scrivener. Chris Strange for putting up with me longer than anyone else. Helen Wiggins for helping me discover my tiny plot of paradise, Hartfield in East Sussex. And lastly to Phil Young for his enthusiasm and sense of fun all those years ago.

Note: some names and places in this book have been changed to protect anonymity – after all, not everyone wants to be accused of being as mad as the Mythbusters are!

Contents

Over the past six years, there have been two hundred and seven Mythbuster cases. In many of them nothing remotely interesting happened. In these four, something did . . .

Introduction

HOW WE BECAME
THE MYTHBUSTERS

Mythbusting is the most brilliant career in the whole world. You can find yourself walking along sandy, palm-fringed beaches in the South Pacific with a treasure map in your hands, searching for pirates' gold, or you could be in the South American jungle, clambering among huge blocks of stone, some weighing a hundred tonnes, investigating the remnants of the mysterious age of the Incas. Or even riding on horseback in a great Californian forest when you spot Bigfoot!

But how did I end up in such an unusual profession? How did the Mythbusters actually begin? I have always been fascinated by the unknown, I suppose. And strange, inexplicable things always seemed to happen to me.

As a very small boy I lived in a sleepy village called Wallington in the English county of Hampshire. I was playing in the nearby Water Meadows where the stalks of ragwort stood taller than me. From the field behind came the sound of men hammering as the first building was erected in what is now, all these years later, an industrial

1

estate. In the meadows ahead was the roar of mechanical diggers and steamrollers and trucks carrying great lengths of concrete pipe, preparations for the new motorway. It is here I saw diminutive creatures with pointed chins and eyes without pupils. They were swarming down from the trees and scurrying away along the river bank. As I watched them, unseen, I sensed they were leaving and would never return to the Water Meadows again.

Who knows exactly what I saw that day, long ago in the 1960s? Perhaps it was only a small boy's feverish imaginings. But I'm sure it wasn't. We'll probably never know. One thing is for sure ... I'd had my first unofficial Mythbusting expedition, and I was thrilled by the experience.

When I was ten years old, I met someone who was to become my very good friend, Chris Strange, in a school playground in Australia. Like me he was English, but his parents had moved to Melbourne. Also like me his favourite topics of conversation were ghosts, monsters and UFOs. We had many boyhood adventures, too numerous to relate here; but in 1980, aged fourteen, while staying at his parents' holiday house at Woodend in the country, Strange and I conducted our first investigation (although we weren't yet called Mythbusters).

Nestling snugly in the folds of surrounding hills, Woodend is what you would call 'sheep country', sunburnt grassland interspersed with isolated patches of eucalypts. Strange's parents, Jean and Fred, had taken us out for a meal to the local pub, 'The Pig and Whistle'. It was here that one of the old regular drinkers told us, two wide-eyed, enthralled boys, about the Werewolf of Woodend. I noticed that he had an enormously swollen, purplycoloured nose with loads of tiny broken veins all over it.

The man told us that, the previous night while he was walking home, a dark shape with huge teeth and glittering red eyes had suddenly appeared from out of the fields. When it saw him, it let out a terrifying, high-pitched squeal and chased him down the road. 'It was too much for a man my age,' he said. 'Too much.'

The disbelieving barman, who'd also been listening to the old man's story, said, 'Too much to drink, you mean!'

But we knew better and, undaunted, set about trying to persuade Strange's parents to let us stay up all night looking for the werewolf. After half an hour's pleading, whining and a false promise that we would not use Fred's pride and joy, a Mercedes Benz, as the stumps in any more cricket matches, we heard those golden words: 'Oh, all right then.'

Hooray! Armed with a stout stick each and a torch, we headed off into werewolf-haunted country. Strange, who never forgot his all-important stomach, somehow managed to conjure up a container full of mixed bean salad. 'It's an emergency midnight snack, mate,' he explained, shamefaced.

The unlit road was very spooky, and every sheep that moved in the surrounding fields we imagined to be the dreaded Werewolf of Woodend. We hadn't been walking along the road for more than ten minutes when the snuffling sounds began.

We didn't think anything of this gentle noise at first. Until I swung a torch in its direction. To reveal a great dark silhouette. We just stood there, mouths open. I don't think we had *really* expected to find anything.

We could see the werewolf pushing its snout into

the mud at the side of the road. Small tusks shone in the pale moonlight. Then it saw us. Fixed us with an evil, beady little eye. Made a horrible, piercing squeal. And charged straight for us. 'Run away!' Strange screamed, and we did.

When we finally limped home to our beds, we were elated. We'd solved the mystery of the Werewolf of Woodend. The 'werewolf' was only a bush pig! Next morning we even told our tale to a woman from the local newspaper. It was amazing. Now we were celebrities as well. From this moment on we were totally 'hooked' on Mythbusting . . .

We were soon wanting to attempt far more ambitious adventures, uncover the answers to far more vexing questions. Like, is the photograph taken at Loch Ness in 1933 by Hugh Gray really the Loch Ness Monster? Or the ghost on the stairs at Raynham Hall in Norfolk, captured on film in 1936, from the spirit world? Are Roger Patterson's movie shots of Bigfoot in 1967 at Bluff Creek, California, fakes? A whole new world of mystery and adventure beckoned us.

And by January 1988 we were in Scotland searching for the Loch Ness Monster. We called ourselves the Myth-busters, poured our savings into this exciting project so that we could rent an office in the United Kingdom which became our nerve-centre, Mythbase (UK)-3. We bought a car to transport us to each weird location. Mabel the Mythmachine, a battered old Morris Minor, was such a character she soon became almost one of the team. She had the amazing knack of never working properly but never quite breaking down. Well, almost never . . .!

What followed was a series of fantastic adventures, as you'll soon discover. But there were a few boring times too. For example, you'll never read stories about 'The Dragon of St Leonard's Forest' or 'UFOs over Avebury Stones'. We spent weeks at these places, and nothing happened. Nothing. Not a sniff of a myth. It goes like that sometimes.

We also uncovered some hoaxes. And some practical jokers. Like the time we conducted a 'corn circle' investigation in France — and found that the crop had been flattened in the shape of a giant question mark!

As investigations took us increasingly worldwide, an Australian office was opened, Mythbase (Oz)-1, and a slightly more reliable vehicle, the four-wheel-drive Myth-rover, was added. Ian Digweed also joined the team at around this time, 1991. Initially hired as the driver of our 'getaway' cars, he soon became more famous in our team for falling over and for having a remarkable ability to run away at great speed from anything interesting.

Although not featured in this book, the most recent addition to our Mythbuster 'family' is Andy Barber, already a well-known television presenter in the United Kingdom for his zany cult cookery programme, *Get Stuffed*.

So currently the team is:

Bowvayne
(leader, writer)

Chris Strange
(researcher, photographer, worrier)

Ian Digweed
(driver, coward)

Andy Barber
(technical expert, cook)

And plans are being made for a third Mythbusters office, Mythbase (US)-1, our very own base in the United States of America, scene of countless mysteries.

MEET THE MYTHBUSTERS

Bowvayne

Eternal optimist. Enthusiastic about Mythbusters to the point of lunacy! Daring — but sometimes foolhardy. Not usually allowed to drive the Mythvehicles. He is slim with long, slightly curly hair that frames a foxy face. Brown eyes. Loves pancakes, chicken drumsticks and practical jokes. Ambitions include (a) wanting to visit another planet to find amazing new life-forms and (b) discovering where pens go once you put them down.

Ian Digweed

Generally incompetent. Clumsy. Accident-prone. Graceful as a hippopotamus in stilettos walking a tightrope. Expert in impaling himself on fences, doing silly walks and stalling cars. He joined the Mythbusters as the official driver of its 'getaway' cars. Skinny, a little over six feet tall. Short, dark-brown hair and a mighty beak of a nose. Ambition is to travel in space.

Chris Strange

Fusspot. Likes to dot every 'i' and cross every 't'. Puppy-dog blue eyes. Slightly receding, short brown hair. Slim, six feet tall. Renowned glutton. Will eat anything that doesn't move – and sometimes things that do. On his days off he pampers himself with mixed bean salads, ice-creams, jam and scones and likes nothing more than passing the time with his bulldog, Nero. Practical by nature, his pockets are always crammed with everything from sherbet ('to keep the sugar levels up') to complex technological gadgets.

Just one more thing before the adventures begin. If you continue to read beyond this point, that ordinary, solid world of yours will vanish completely as if by a conjuror's sleight of hand – and a far more mysterious reality will be revealed. You have been warned.

Bowvayne
Sumatra, 1995

1. Clapham Wood

MYTHBUSTERS CASE FILE

TITLE: Clapham Wood

CODE: 002E 010888

LOCATION: Clapham Wood, Sussex,
                  England

MYTHBUSTERS: Bowvayne
                  Chris Strange

TERRAIN: Ancient woodlands,
                  surrounded by steep slopes
                  and flat farm fields

DIFFICULTIES: Investigating the thick
                  woodland after dark

MISSION: Full-scale investigation. To
                  attempt to find a common
                  thread through the differing
                  mysteries, including
                  disappearances, UFOs and
                  other paranormal events

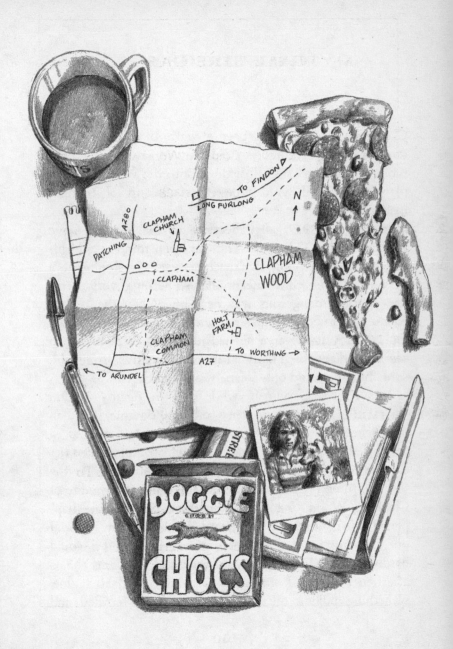

CASE HISTORY

Clapham Wood has long been a centre of mystery. Over two hundred years ago, an old woman saw what would today be called a UFO float down into the wood, and the place was 'filled with fumes that stinketh of burning matter'.

In August 1977, after hearing all the stories, Dave Stringer visited the wood 'with an open mind' – and his Geiger counter. Soon the machine was registering at a very high rate, which meant that something very weird and possibly dangerous was near by. When the Geiger counter returned to registering normal measurements, he looked back at the area he had just been through ... to see an indistinct, ghostly shape four metres in height, something he could only describe as a 'black mass'.

Mrs K. M. Goodman, who lived in nearby Findon Valley, also has a strange story to tell. She wrote, 'I had an experience a few years ago.' Mrs Goodman drove up to the top of the hill above Findon cricket ground, parked her car and took her dog for a walk up the cart track. At the top, she turned right – and eventually came to the edge of Clapham Wood. But then something inexplicable happened. She continued: 'I had heard about Clapham Wood. I put the dog on her lead and turned back. But I could hardly move. My legs felt as if they had balls and chains attached to them. I struggled yard after yard at a time, something pulling me back. My dog was terrified and pulled on her lead.' After she had battled against this force for about fifty metres, it subsided. She added, 'I never went near the wood again!'

Then there are reports of mysterious mists suddenly appearing and manifesting themselves into predatory animals. Spectral bears, wolves and foxes have all been reported.

A 'Bermuda Triangle', comprising Long Furlong, the A27 Arundel Road and Cote Street and including Clapham Wood, has been the centre of UFO mysteries for many years. In October 1987, Durrington insurance clerk Mark Green spotted a strange yellow light over the South Downs. Green, eighteen years old at the time, said, 'It sort of stretched as if it was trying to break apart. It was as though some invisible hand was playing with plasticine – I assumed it was a supernova.'

But surely one of the most bizarre Clapham Wood mysteries involves dogs disappearing without trace. In February 1988 Rex Congdon reported that his dog had vanished while he was walking through the wood. 'I took my dog for a walk in the wood and she came over all peculiar,' he said. 'We were going along the path when she suddenly ran round in ever decreasing circles, howling the whole time. Then she shot through the trees and I never saw her again.'

John Cornford also told how his normally obedient collie suddenly raced off, never to be seen again. Mr and Mrs Peter Love of Clapham said their chow just disappeared. 'Our son took him for his usual walk in the woods and the dog went into an outcrop of trees. Usually he comes out the other side, but this time he didn't. He completely vanished.'

There was already enough of a Clapham Wood 'Case History' for the Mythbusters to mount several investigations. Then came the Marjorie Medhurst incident . . .

ONE

The late afternoon sun beats down from a cloudless sky. Can this be England? The British call it a heatwave. Everyone else calls it 'a relief from eleven and a half months of miserable weather'.

CLAPHAM VILLAGE is the sign that greets you as you climb eastwards out of one of the South Downs' valleys. Darkly framing the sign is Clapham Wood, a sinister place of twisted, stunted trees whose branches and brambles grab and hold and seem to want to keep you there. Big hollow oaks are being slowly strangled by parasitic ivy. Bracken and stinging nettles hide a hundred natural pitfalls. Apart from the occasional crow's 'caw', the wood is silent. Still. And full of dark secrets.

Marjorie Medhurst is taking her Labrador-cross for a walk along one of Clapham Wood's shady tracks. She is a petite woman, aged about forty-five, with shoulder-length chestnut hair and striking blue eyes. Mrs Medhurst often takes long rambles through the wood with her dog, Trixie. She knows the place has a weird reputation, but she doesn't believe in all that 'supernatural nonsense'.

As they walk through a small copse, known to the locals as The Chestnuts, Trixie is the first to sense something unusual. She stops at a tree, sniffing and snuffling. Then snuffling and sniffing.

The dog becomes distressed; she wipes her snout on the grass, as if ridding herself of something nasty. Then

15

she begins to howl dementedly.

Mrs Medhurst feels something, too: incredible pressure on her eardrums . . . terrible stomach cramp. Some invisible force has her in its grip.

The dog races off between the trees, her tail between her legs. Heading north to the fields and thicker woods. The woman tries to follow her pet, but the psychic forces hold her back. The abnormal physical forces gradually lessen. But she's too late. Trixie is gone.

Mrs Medhurst returns home. There are tears in her eyes. She calls Mythbusters.

Bowvayne pulls off his boots and sighs with relief. He collapses into a bean-bag and stares distractedly around the room at the framed pictures of Sai Baba, Sigmund Freud and Daffy Duck and the glass display case that houses an amazing collection of tropical frogs, toads and newts. There is an overstuffed look to the place, with too many whiteboards, bean-bags and televisions. There are three sofas, designed to double up as pull-out drawers, which are overflowing with research. This is the office/lounge-room of Mythbase (UK)-3, the top-secret headquarters and nerve-centre of the Mythbusters' entire European operation. Well, it had been a secret headquarters until Bowvayne telephoned for pizza one evening. It is a flat above a newsagent's, overlooking a car park.

Finally he says, 'Phew! What a day, Phil. Phil?'

A tall, balding man in his late thirties is asleep on the office settee. Once a well-known disc-jockey on pirate and offshore radio, this is Phil Young, a local expert on a temporary assignment with the Mythbusters.

It has been a busy week. Unbelievable. Fifteen jobs!

Capturing seven capybaras (giant South American rodents) that somehow managed to escape from their owner in a sleepy English village. Investigating numerous ghost sightings. Searching for treasure after a client found an old map in his attic. (Bowvayne and Chris Strange were soon digging in a nearby park and discovered a tea-chest full of 'fruity' love-letters belonging to the client's great-grandfather!) Strange is still away on an 'off-the-record' job at a certain military establishment which is supposed to be haunted.

Bowvayne glances at the whiteboard. He groans. There are four more jobs listed under his name. Beneath Young's name is written, 'Jobs completed. Money collected. In my back pocket.' Bowvayne chuckles. Young's a typical DJ, he'll do anything for you — if the money's right.

The telephone hotline brooooooops. Young rolls over and picks it up in his sleep. 'Room service?' His voice is deep and stagey. A pause. Then he wakes up. 'Er . . . Mythbusters. Young speaking.

'A lost dog . . . Trixie . . . Clapham Wood . . . Box of "DOGGIE CHOCS" . . . We're on our way, madam!'

Bowvayne and Young race down the narrow stairs and pile into Mabel the Mythmachine, which is parked outside.

'We've got a hot one here,' says Young. His face is like a cunning wolf with very dark-brown eyes. He guns the engine. She refuses to start. He tries again. Mabel whines pitifully.

Bowvayne is clearly unimpressed. 'We could always trade her in for something more useful.'

'Like what?'

'Like bus passes!'

Mabel the Mythmachine is obviously stung by Bowvayne's criticism. She suddenly jerks forward. The Mythbusters are on their way.

TWO

It is one of those enchanting English scenes that must have inspired William Shakespeare to write poetry. The merest warm orange sliver, like a piece of marmalade rind, hints at where the whole of the sun had been. There is the gentlest breeze on this warm and balmy evening. Rabbits play and box one another's ears. Blackbirds sing. Swallows line the telephone wires. Bats flap around an old church steeple.

Bowvayne and Young seem unaware of the scene. In fact they're going a long way towards spoiling it. The graceless Mythmachine is making explosive 'phut-phutting' sounds all the way up the road. Thick oily clouds pour from the stricken car.

Young curses as Mabel stalls again and he cracks his head against the windscreen. 'This car has got to go!'

Mabel finally staggers to a halt on a grassy verge by the busy Long Furlong road. They take walkie-talkies, torches and a box of Trixie's favourite 'DOGGIE CHOCS' from the boot.

Bowvayne smiles when he notices Strange has 'sticky-labelled' every item with the sober message: 'HAVE YOU CHECKED THIS ITEM OUT ON YOUR EQUIPMENT LIST?' He wonders idly whether Strange has put stickers on each individual dog chocolate too. Then, flicking on his walkie-talkie, Bowvayne says, 'Are you there, "Echo Charlie"? Over.' The reason Echo Charlie has such an unusual nickname soon becomes obvious.

'This is Echo Charlie. Echo Charlie. Go ahead.' The voice hisses and crackles through the machine in the Mythbuster's hand. 'This is Echo Charlie. Go ahead.'

'We're just about to go into the wood. Over.'

'Thank you, Echo-One.'

A compact little man in his fifties, Echo Charlie is the local ham-radio wizard. His car is parked in a lay-by on the A280, a road that runs parallel and to the north of the route the pair will take. The car is fitted out with all the latest communication equipment, and a ten-metre-high radio mast is lashed to its side. The words 'EMERGENCY CONTROL' are stuck on the windscreen. He acts as a sort of safety officer: should anything go wrong, he will know immediately.

Bowvayne and Young are taking no chances. There are too many mysterious disappearances and strange stories about Clapham Wood for them to go unprepared. Echo Charlie has to inform the police of the Mythbusters' presence – even they consider it to be pretty spooky.

The time now is 8 p.m. The air is cool – and full of mosquitoes. The pair cross the road, climb over the stile and march up the steep slope that leads into Clapham Wood.

They pass beneath the long shadows of the trees. Into a bracken clearing. It is still too light to use torches.

'Trixie!' yells Young.

'Trixie!' yells Bowvayne.

'Chockies!' yells Young.

'Chockies!' yells Bowvayne.

(They call 'Trixie' and offer 'chockies' so many times in

the next couple of hours that repeating it would probably fill this book.)

'Trixie!'

'Chockies!'

(But you're sure to have got the idea.)

'Mmmmm! These chocolates aren't bad!' says Young, flicking one in the air and catching it in his mouth.

'Yuck!' cries Bowvayne, looking appalled.

'What I could really do with is a cup of tea and a piece of cake!'

'Or a nice juicy bone!' quips Bowvayne. 'But I must admit, I'm pretty hungry too. Are you sure those dog chocolates are OK . . .?'

Dusk descends quickly. The only sound is the screeching of an owl. They reach the edge of the north section of the wood, jump across a deep ditch and climb over a barbed-wire fence. The pair begin to cross the fields that separate the northern part from the tree'd area to the south — where The Chestnuts is situated.

'Not a sign of the dog. I'll bet that . . .' Bowvayne stops. Young's face has turned to a ghastly pallor. His mouth opening and closing like a fish's — but no sound is coming out.

Finally he manages to point to his left and say, 'Bull!'

Bowvayne takes a glance and wishes he hadn't. This is a huge bull: the Minotaur's big brother. He scratches the ground with his front hoof, getting ready to charge. His horns catch the moonlight. They gleam evilly, like curved Arabian swords . . .

'Run!' screams Young. A rather unnecessary thing to say as they have both been running for some time.

Maybe he won't get them. Only two hundred metres

to the next fence. The bull thunders after the pair. Maybe he will get them. They're nearly at the fence. But the charging bull is moving like an express train. He's bound to get one of them. Bowvayne hopes he gets Young. Young hopes he gets Bowvayne. They can smell the bull's hot, snorting breath now. Practically feel those terrible horns . . . Suddenly, there is a scream: 'Aaaaaaaaaaah!'

THREE

'Let's sit down for a couple of minutes,' Bowvayne suggests.

'You can. I'll just keep standing.' Young clutches his buttocks tenderly.

It is a week later. The pair are back at Clapham Wood, with the TVS *Coast To Coast* television programme's reporter and film crew. They are between 'takes'.

The excellent — but slightly sceptical — television journalist, Shelley Hunt, is doing a story on the Mythbusters and their Clapham Wood investigation.

The camera rolls. She says, 'If you go down to Clapham Wood, you'd better not go alone. Mysterious things have been known to happen there. People hear weird noises. See strange things. And dogs completely disappear!

'But now Mythbusters are here . . .'

It is Young's turn. Arms folded, he says to the reporter who is standing in front of the camera, 'Loads and loads of dogs over the decades have gone missing [in Clapham Wood] — never to be seen again!' He recounts the latest mysterious canine disappearance: that of Trixie, belonging to Mrs Medhurst.

Shelley Hunt moves on to the next subject. 'Bow and Phil have already tracked down one eye-witness, who claims he saw a balloon-like UFO over the wood.' He is forty-five-year-old Tony Whittick, who takes up the story.

'It [the UFO] changed shape. The light – the luminosity – appeared to come from within it. It didn't move in the sky for some considerable time. We had it in view for twenty to twenty-five minutes.'

Then, explaining the difficulties of such an investigation, Young makes the valid point that, 'Anything can happen at any time. When people "see strange things", they haven't gone out purposely looking for them like we are . . .'

Bowvayne is asked what he thinks is behind the mysteries of Clapham Wood. He frowns. '. . . It may be some ancient pagan site. They had a "way" with energy that we don't have these days. I think it could be something like that, drawing all sorts of different things to the one spot . . .'

Now it is the director's turn. He wipes the sweat from his brow. It is a hot day. 'I'd like a few shots of you walking through the wood.' He gives Bowvayne and Young some sound advice. 'No silly walks! Don't go too quickly. Pass the camera in about twenty seconds. And don't look at the camera . . .'

They walk past at a funereal pace. The director says, 'Thank you. That's fine. Thank you.'

In the months following the story going on air, the intrepid investigators receive hundreds of telephone calls and letters. But, sadly, Trixie is never found.

FOUR

It is a freezing January night, five months after Trixie's disappearance and the television interview.

Mabel the Mythmachine clatters down the motorway towards the city of Portsmouth, still held together in one piece by a coat of rust and a few kind words. (Mabel, that is, not Portsmouth!)

'Come on. Come on, old girl!' mutters Strange. 'If you speed up a bit I won't take you to the scrap heap next week.' And other kind words like that.

Inside, Bowvayne, Young and Strange, who has long since returned from the 'off-the-record job', are abuzz with enthusiasm. They have their first real Clapham Wood lead for months.

Bowvayne is first out of the car, already striding through the gate of the little semi-detached house in a Portsmouth backwater. Young is close behind. But Strange is fiddling about with a new 'bottom-warmer' he has installed on the driver's seat. Bowvayne knocks on the peeling, red-painted front door. There is a little shower of red specks ... but no answer.

'That's strange,' says Strange, joining them. 'After all, he did invite us.'

Young isn't so surprised. 'He sounded an odd character on the phone.'

Strange knocks on the door this time. Lights come on in the hall. The front door swings open and the trio are overwhelmed by a pack of panting standard poodles. With hangdog looks, the Mythbusters wipe poodle-curls and

23

doggie-slobber from their faces.

'You must be the Mythbusters,' says an elderly man, who is holding bowls of dog food. 'Please come inside.'

When the dogs are safely locked away in the laundry room, they sit in a small, book-cluttered lounge, sipping coffee. Tall and spindly, aged about seventy, Reg Stevenson has a nose so long and curved it would be better suited as a wading-bird's bill. It is so huge they find it hard not to stare. And if that's not bad enough, he keeps mentioning noses all the time as well.

'. . . As you knows, I nosed around Clapham Wood for nearly thirty years, before I moved down here last year. Collected all the stories. Something of a local expert, I am.' He points at himself proudly.

Strange is impatient. They've travelled a long way this evening. 'What is this vital information you mentioned on the phone?'

Stevenson isn't going to be rushed. He wants to have his moment of glory. 'No one could discover the truth of the weird occurrences. No one could work it out. Except me. I have a nose for the truth . . .'

The Mythbusters smother smiles. Tackle titters. He has a nose for everything.

But Stevenson knows a couple of things about Clapham Wood that the Mythbusters don't – and it is vital information. He talks in a hushed, dramatic tone. 'I know what happened to Marjorie Medhurst's dog! And I know what happened to all the others . . .' Stevenson pauses for effect. Entranced, the Mythbusters and Young lean forward. Tension mounts. Then rides away. 'They were devoured by the unknown forces that lurk in Clapham Wood. And I think it has to do with ley-lines. You see, Clapham is the connecting point for leys coming from Chanctonbury Ring to Cissbury Ring, also places of mystery and weird activity in the area. Do you know what leys are?'

'A line joining two prominent points in the landscape, thought to be the line of a prehistoric track,' Strange intones, as if he's memorized the whole thing, word for word, from a book.

'Yes! Yes! But a ley is so much more than that!' Stevenson says, becoming animated. 'Natural earth energy flows along these unseen ancient pathways. Our ancestors knew the secret of using this powerful source. It enabled them to do amazing things, such as alter the weather and communicate telepathically with people in the next village; at least, this is what a lot of us believe. You must remember, this was in the days when Magic was the reality and Science unheard of. In this modern scientific age we scoff at words like "magic", and consequently have forgotten how to use the power of the ley-lines . . .'

Bowvayne's eyes have a fanatical gleam as Stevenson continues. 'But this is the most important part. There is a sect in the wood who for the past few years have been trying to relearn the secrets of our forebears. But in their ignorance of the workings of the leys, they are inadvertently unleashing strange forces. These appear as pure energy, weird lights and apparitions.'

Young gulps nervously. 'Have you ever seen these things yourself?'

'Yes, many times. And some of them exude an awesome power.'

Strange's face clouds over. 'So we're in pretty dangerous territory, then.' Young nods in agreement.

But the madcap Bowvayne seems unaware of the

25

possibly fatal consequences. Waving his arms about excitedly, he declares, 'Mythbusters will bust this one tonight!'

FIVE

'This is Echo Charlie. Echo Charlie. I read you loud and clear, Echo-One,' says . . . (you guessed right, it's Echo Charlie!)

Bowvayne presses the button of his walkie-talkie again. 'Yeah, Echo Charlie. This is our fifteen-minute "OK" call. We're at the northernmost tip of the wood . . . we think.'

The Mythbusters have climbed up the Long Furlong slope and are beneath the trees. What a night it's been. First the poodles! Then Stevenson's revelations. And now the unknown awaits them . . .

They are heavily laden with gear: miners' hard hats with headlamps attached, audio tape-recorders fixed to their belts, cameras round their necks. Backpacks containing spare batteries and tapes, medical supplies, camera film, specimen jars, walkie-talkies and a Geiger counter.

Strange is carrying the Geiger counter. It is a device for detecting and counting ionizing particles in order to measure radioactivity.

Bowvayne and Young let him carry it because he is the only one who knows what the last sentence means. In plain language, the Geiger counter is the Mythbusters' weirdness detector. If it gives a high reading, something unexplained is about.

A rabbit darts out in front of them and disappears at speed. 'I wonder what he's seen that we don't know about!' Bowvayne says, only half-seriously.

An unknown force that devours animals. A pagan sect. The other two give Bowvayne a sour look. 'I don't know how you talked me into this foolishness tonight, mate,' Strange mutters fussily. 'We haven't planned it properly or anything.' Bowvayne knows that Strange is grumpy because he's forgotten his lunchbox full of mixed bean salad.

The Geiger counter makes a crackling sound.

'Hey! I'm getting an unbelievable reading on this . . .' An instant later, Strange staggers forward and collapses on the ground. Bowvayne sinks to his knees with a sickening moan, clutching his head.

Young is frantic. 'Echo Charlie! Echo Charlie! We . . .' He doubles over, his stomach racked with painful spasms.

The walkie-talkie explodes into life. 'Echo-One! Echo-One! Do you require assistance, Echo-One?'

But there is no reply.

SIX

'Echo-One! Do you require assistance?' asks Echo Charlie from the safe haven of the lay-by on the A280. If they don't answer this time, he'll call the police.

Inside the wood, Bowvayne rubs his head gingerly. 'Negative. Negative, Echo Charlie. We're all right now. But we must have just experienced some of those odd physical effects that have been widely reported. For no apparent reason this "force" struck. And for no apparent reason it went.'

'I feel as if my brains have turned into soup,' Young cuts in.

'. . . We're marching south. Over and out.'

'Thank you, Echo-One. Echo Charlie standing by.'

The Mythbusters decide to keep going. If what Stevenson told them is true, the best is yet to come. And anyway, the Mythmachine is waiting for them down at The Chestnuts.

They reach the edge of the wood. Jump a ditch. Climb a barbed-wire fence. Cross the fields. Young hopes the famous bull has moved on to greener pastures, preferably in Outer Mongolia.

They take a flying leap across another ditch, clearing it easily. And find themselves standing knee-deep in oozy mud on the far side. The trio slosh and squelch along a driveway, vault an electrified fence and veer off to the left, into the tree'd area of Clapham Wood. They are relieved to discover a footpath. A fall could mean a broken leg among the trees in here.

Young squints at his map. 'This is The Chestnuts – definitely.'

Bowvayne points to something his headlamp is illuminating. 'Look at this!'

Floating in front of them are three red dots forming a triangle, the whole thing no bigger than the face of a woman's watch. Just as Stevenson had said . . .

'Fleeting pinpoints on the edge of vision,' Bowvayne says poetically.

They all photograph this weird phenomenon. Strange takes a reading with the Geiger counter. 'It's up again . . .' The 'pinpoints' blink. Are gone. '. . . and now it's dropped down again!'

The three dots reappear behind the Mythbusters. Drift slowly downward. Blink. Disappear again. It seems to be a single entity. Now it's darting above the treetops.

After watching this lively, eccentric performance for fifteen minutes or so, the trio move away down the track, looking for anything else out of the ordinary. A metal gate comes into view. The Mythmachine waits for them on the other side, not fifty metres away. The 'pinpoints' follow.

Bowvayne is jubilant. 'This is absolutely unbelievable! We've found something here that I'm at a loss to explain . . .'

Strange considers the practical side. 'I'm not looking forward to explaining it. You can just imagine what people will say when we come out of here and start babbling about little red dots. They'll think we're crazy!'

They quicken their pace. The triangle of dots speeds up too. Bowvayne stops. He studies it again. It stays with him.

Strange and Young reach the gate, climb over and wait for him. He is perhaps twenty metres up the track.

Young is about to call Echo Charlie. Suddenly a feeling of evil pours over him. As if he's been injected with liquid night. He shudders as the chill creeps through his body. He's totally spooked by it. 'Get out of there! Bow! Get out!' he bellows.

Bowvayne does something strange: he just smiles. Why is Phil making such a fuss? After all, he's only looking at three little dots . . .

But Bowvayne can't see what the other two can see now.

Strange and Young's torches capture a side-view of the 'pinpoints'. It surpasses everything Stevenson had told them. It is a vast, shapeless mass with flickering red moving along its length in waves. Like energy in physical form. It is a sinister, spectral red. But, at the same time, you can see right through it.

The weird form seems to be crouching – ready to spring . . .

'Get out of there, you idiot!'

But all Bowvayne can see is three little dots . . .

SEVEN

Bowvayne seems bewitched. He stumbles blindly towards the tree where the entity lurks. Three little dots . . .

Strange and Young are clearly terrified. But Strange takes command. He grabs the Geiger counter, then switches on his headlamp. 'Phil, get the car started. I'm going in.'

Swallowing nervously, he climbs over the gate and whispers into the walkie-talkie, 'Echo Charlie. Echo Charlie. This is Echo-One. Do you read me? Over.'

'Roger, Echo-One. This is Echo Charlie. Echo Charlie. Go ahead, Echo-One.'

'We've found something. Something inexplicable. And it looks very, very dangerous. Bowvayne could be in trouble. I'm going in. Be ready to call the police and an ambulance immediately.'

'Roger, Echo-One.'

Strange steps forward cautiously. Like someone who's dropped their car-keys in a crocodile's mouth. His lamp casts eerie shadows along the track. He moves closer. Closer. Closer . . .

He joins Bowvayne.

'Let's move it,' Strange hisses urgently, glancing fearfully at the three 'pinpoints' twinkling innocently. From here, they're just three little dots ... but he knows better. The Geiger counter crackles insanely — jammed on maximum.

Bowvayne replies, almost dreamily, 'It's as if it's trying to suck my mind from my body ...' He casually passes his hand through the 'pinpoints'.

Strange's eyes widen in horror. The paranormal manifestation sizzles. The odour of hot electric wires fills the air. It appears to be angry. Very angry.

Face bathed in sweat, Strange drags Bowvayne by the shoulders. Back along the track. Then babbles into the walkie-talkie, 'Echo Charlie! We're getting out of here! Fast!'

They reach the gate. Bowvayne shakes his head from side to side. 'I feel like I've just awoken from hypnosis or something. What happened?'

'That happened!' Strange screams.

For the first time Bowvayne's headlamp reveals the true extent of the apparition to him. 'Wow! Unbelievable!' He is awed — and afraid. It is a huge, trans-dimensional 'creature'. This flickering red entity assumes a more menacing posture.

Young is revving the car's engine. Bowvayne and Strange are about to climb back over the gate, but then they notice something weird. The 'Clapparition' seems to be altering ... shape-shifting. Tensing like a coiled spring.

Without warning, it roars towards them like a raging fireball. A hot wind hits the pair. They shriek and scramble over the gate with fear-weakened limbs, just as the Clapparition hits them.

It oozes through the gate — and re-forms.

Bowvayne and Strange bundle into the car. 'Go-go-go, Phil!' they scream.

The car cuts out completely. No power. Nothing.

The Clapparition billows across the windscreen. Will it come into the Mythmachine? There's no way they're going to hang around and find out.

Three doors fly open. Three bodies scramble out of Mabel and into the road on all fours. Then run. And run. And run.

Finally, they slow down. Exhausted. 'Hang on. Where are we?' asks Young.

'Paris, I think!' Bowvayne jokes, gasping and wheezing, trying to catch his breath.

In the distance they can see the Clapparition, hovering by the edge of the road. It seems to be studying them. Summing them up. Warning them . . .

Then it vanishes.

Strange switches on his walkie-talkie. 'Echo Charlie. Echo Charlie. This is Echo-One. Come and pick us up, please. We're all right — for now . . .'

Artist's impression of the Clapparition

CASE CLOSING NOTES

There is definitely a strange force in Clapham Wood. And consider this: *The Clapparition must exist in a different dimension from the one we live in.* No creature in human experience can be so small and so large at the same time.

It is this entity that is somehow responsible for the so-called UFO sightings – and all the other mysteries. But of the pagan sect that were supposedly behind the Clapparition the Mythbusters found no evidence this time.

No creature in human experience can cause such odd physical effects.

No creature in human experience can ruin three separate cameras' film. There were no pictures on the Mythbusters' three cameras, just a blinding white haze, which even professional photographers were at a loss to explain.

Oh, and one more thing. Hidden among the hours and hours of audio-taping the Mythbusters took while in Clapham Wood is something very creepy. Although they heard nothing at the time, agonized screams are scattered throughout the recording.

2. The Ghost and the Graveyard

MYTHBUSTERS CASE FILE

TITLE: The Ghost and the Graveyard

CODE: 001Oz 301091

LOCATION: The Melbourne Cemetery, Victoria, Australia

MYTHBUSTERS: Bowvayne
Ian Digweed
Chris Strange

TERRAIN: Roughly a kilometre square of gently undulating ground, comprising long grass and weathered gravestones

DIFFICULTIES: Investigating the stone-cluttered, uneven ground after dark

MISSION: To establish whether Red Rogan's ghost really exists. To photograph it with spirit cameras

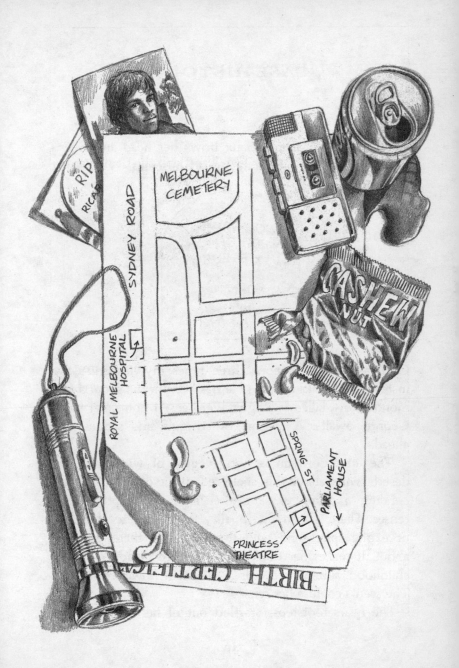

CASE HISTORY

Young dancer Marie Le Saux bows her head and weeps before the gravestone of her dead husband. Why didn't

GOD GIVETH
GOD TAKETH AWAY
JACQUES LE SAUX

BORN 1866
DIED 1891
R.I.P.

God take away someone three times my husband's age instead, she thinks bitterly. He has been in the ground two months now, killed in a fight over her. At home, her baby, George, awaits. A lifetime of struggle and sadness lies ahead.

The afternoon sun is hot. A gust of wind from the desert swirls about this sheltered patch of the cemetery, bending a clump of skinny eucalypts. Abruptly Marie tenses. There is a strange quality to the breeze, the smell of exotic spices and wild flowers, as if there is magic about. It makes her think of the French meadows of her childhood: autumn orchards . . . the first flowers of spring. The scents confuse her senses . . .

She hears footsteps. Startled out of her thoughts, she

spins around. A tall, dark-haired man is standing before her, eyes like emeralds and with something Romany in his appearance. He is the most handsome man she has ever seen. His smile is so dazzling it warms her heart. Then she is afraid. Where has she seen him before? There is certainly a strange magic at work here. She *should* recognize him, as she knows this man well – but, for now, she doesn't.

He smiles again, dispelling her fears. 'Come now, you must mourn no more. You will not bring him back. Jacques is quite content to wait for you on The Other Side. You will dwell here on this earth for such a short time that it may as well be a blissful stay . . .'

'H-How do you know my husband?' Marie asks falteringly.

'We were very alike, your husband and I. So much in common. So many struggles for the same things . . .' The whiff of magic is still in the air. 'Would you like me to stay with you awhile and talk?'

Marie nods dreamily. Hypnotized, she allows him to take her arm.

They walk for a short distance and sit beside another new gravestone.

'It is only in money that your husband and I differ: he had it – I did not.' The air is heavy now. But the young dancing girl is captivated by this mysterious man who still hasn't introduced himself. She knows now that she *should* recognize him, and it is a maddening feeling, like forgetting how to spell a really easy word.

But they go on to talk about Jacques, baby George, herself and her dancing. She can't remember ever being so happy. In that moment she wishes they could be together for ever. There could not be another in the world such as he . . .

The shadows of the tombstones grow long. A chill of evening is in the air.

'Have we spoken for so long?' she says in sudden surprise.

'Yes, we have, my love. And now we must part.' Her face fills with grief and pain at the thought of losing him. 'But not for ever, Marie. You must promise to meet me here, at this time, two weeks today, and seal that promise with a kiss.'

He puts his strong arms round her.

'Yes, I *will* come,' she says.

Their lips touch. Now she *knows* who he is. Oh, dear God in Heaven, help me! The man's lips turn hard and bony. The stench of death and decay hangs in the air. She finds herself in the arms of a skeleton.

The truth dawns on her. Yes! She has embraced her husband's killer, who was also killed in the brawl over her. She faints.

An unearthly fever grips her, eventually forcing her to keep her promise to the ghost. On the very day and at the very time she had arranged to meet him, she is taken to the Melbourne Cemetery and buried there.

ONE

Like a flying lizard drifting down from a dawn jungle canopy, the Boeing 747 descends into Tullamarine Airport outside Melbourne, Australia. Mythbuster Bowvayne looks eagerly out of one of its small oval windows. The sunrise is a spectacular gold. He disembarks and wheels his suitcases through Customs.

Outside the terminal, fellow Mythbuster Chris Strange is waiting. 'The plane was seven minutes late,' he says by way of a greeting. He has been back in Australia for several weeks, conducting an initial investigation into 'The Ghost and the Graveyard' case, visiting the site and meeting one of Marie Le Saux's descendants.

'How are you, you old fusspot?' Bowvayne replies affectionately, looking baggy-eyed after the long flight.

'Not bad, apart from dehydration of my cerebral fluid, causing a subsequent and agonizing rubbing of brain on cranium.'

Bowvayne laughs loudly. 'You mean you've got a headache!'

Strange grips his temples and winces.

Struggling with seven heavy suitcases, they head across the car park to the Mythbusters' latest Mythvehicle, a battered, blue-grey, four-wheel-drive Land Rover nicknamed the Mythrover. As Strange tosses the suitcases into the back, he says accusingly, 'Hey, where are your sticky labels? They're supposed to be on your cases.'

'Wrong colour-scheme. They didn't match my luggage,' Bowvayne retorts, quick as a batted eyelid.

'Ah, good point,' Strange concedes. He makes a mental note to look out for tatty-brown-coloured sticky labels. And some faded tartan ones too.

Bowvayne is out of trouble, for now. But he's still got to tell Strange that their matching sandwich boxes and the extra-large mixed bean salad holder are all at the bottom of Loch Ness.

Strange drives them in the direction of Melbourne, a little over half an hour away. The early October morning is becoming grey and overcast, freckled with rain. Bowvayne babbles excitedly about their latest case, a dragon hunt. Strange nods mechanically, concentrating on the driving and his headache.

Soon Bowvayne is being hustled into Mythbase (Oz)-1, the top-secret headquarters and nerve-centre of the Myth-busters' entire Australasian operation; it is a white weatherboard house in Brunswick Street, North Fitzroy, a suburb just outside the city.

'Get inside quick. This place is top secret,' Strange hisses urgently, glancing across at the nearby cricket ground. 'And no telephoning the Pizza Palace Home Delivery Service. I don't want anyone finding out *this* address!' Then he grumbles to himself, tottering inside with all seven cases. His partner follows him.

Soon Bowvayne is sipping a mug of tea and munching on crumpets dripping in melted butter. Contentedly, he sinks deeper into his easy chair.

The room is a mixture of domestic lounge and ancient pagan site. The television and video are covered with bizarre wooden death-masks. An African burial pole seems to sprout from a cheap glass-topped coffee table. Even more incongruously, a set of sacrificial knives from a lost city of the Aztecs is lying next to a poster of Daffy Duck, who is sweating nervously. Only a lunatic could create a room like this.

'The new office is great, isn't it?' Strange says heartily.

'Come on, Chris.' Bowvayne waves his arms about impatiently and leans forward in his chair. 'I've just flown twelve thousand miles. Where's this ghost? Spirited away?'

The vein in the middle of Strange's forehead pumps up as he says excitedly, 'What we have right here in Melbourne is the best chance we'll ever get of sighting, photographing and proving to the world that ghosts really exist. It's remarkably similar to a tale in an old book by Elliott O'Donnell, *Ghosts*, that I discovered during my research. The Le Saux family claims to have been targeted by a spirit for over a hundred years. It seems fairly unlikely that they would know O'Donnell's old story . . .'

'But where?'

Strange pauses for effect. 'Wwwell . . .' he teases. Then, when Bowvayne begins to twitch visibly with frustration, 'The ghost is called Red Rogan. And he haunts Melbourne Cemetery!'

A sudden knock at the door makes Bowvayne jump. 'Are you expecting anyone?'

'Yes, it could very well be the latest Mythbuster! I spoke to him on the phone last week. Phil Young recommends him very highly. He may well be the specialist driver we've been looking for.'

'Is he Australian?'

'No. He's on holiday out here, but he's English.'

Strange answers the door. A hesitant, bumbling figure

43

is framed in the doorway. He is skinny, a little over six feet tall, with short, dark-brown hair and a mighty beak of a nose. Small, round mirror-shades rest on the bridge of the beak and a peak-at-the-back baseball cap give him a rather jaunty appearance. 'I was ... er ... wasn't quite sure where the Mythbusters' office was, so I asked for directions at the Pizza Palace.' He continues to loiter uncertainly.

But the two Mythbusters are affecting their most pompous Mr Employer looks. They have resumed their slouching in easy chairs.

'Name?' asks Bowvayne.

'Ian Digweed.'

'Is that your real name or a pseudonym?'

Digweed is incredulous. 'You've got to be joking. If I was going to choose something other than my real name, it would be Falconer or Buckingham – not Digweed!'

Bowvayne jots this down in his notepad.

It's Strange's turn. 'What makes you think you're qualified for the job, Mr Digweed?'

Digweed relaxes. He's got them now, he thinks. But he says, 'I'm a trained racing-car driver. I've driven on the Formula One Grand Prix courses at Brand's Hatch and Silverstone.'

Four Mythbuster eyebrows arch heavenward. The pair are thinking the same thing: He's only a couple of right answers away from getting the job.

Bowvayne is openly friendly to the 'new boy' now. 'Do sit down. Now what interests you about the unknown?'

'I don't know, because it's unknown. Ha ha ha!'

The Mythbusters write 'clever-dick' in their notepads.

'But seriously,' Digweed continues, 'I've always been fascinated by UFOs. And all those stories about there

44

being extra-terrestrials frozen in ice somewhere right here on Earth.'

'Great! That fascinates me, too,' Bowvayne enthuses.

Strange gives the interviewee his most penetrating stare. 'Do you ever run away or panic under pressure?'

'Occasionally.'

'Good, because we do,' Strange says in a droll tone.

Bowvayne's turn again. 'What else have you done, apart from drive cars?'

'I was a trainee chef . . .' begins Digweed.

'Really?' Strange interrupts, thinking of his all-important stomach. He jumps to his feet excitedly. 'Do you know how to make mixed bean salad or breadfruit curry?'

Bowvayne groans in dismay.

'Yes I do,' Digweed replies, lying.

'You're in, Mr Digweed,' says Strange, vigorously shaking hands with him.

TWO

The Melbourne night is cool and still and full of stars. An old green tram clatters to a halt with all the grace of a pneumatic drill. Richelle Le Saux clambers aboard, adjusting the rucksack on her shoulders. It is just another night of psychic investigation for this seventeen-year-old student and hitherto non-believer in ghosts and scoffer at spirits. This is the descendant of Marie's whom Strange met the week before.

Her family have told her of an evil ghost that killed her great-grandmother a hundred years before, and of a curse that falls upon any member of the Le Sauxs who visits the cemetery. Not that Richelle believes a word of it.

But, to this intelligent, inquisitive girl whose half-term entertainment normally consists of discos and talking about boys, investigating this ancient family legend draws her like a Venus fly-trap does a fly.

She scales the tall cemetery fence and lands on the other side with the sure grace of a cat. Then, taking a hand-drawn map and a torch from her rucksack, she creeps forward. This is the eleventh time she has trespassed into the graveyard after dark, but she still checks the map, since it becomes a bewildering place late at night. Carefully onward. She's close now.

Suddenly, she has a psychic inkling. Something strange, inexplicable and spooky is about to happen . . .

And then she spots something! At first it is just the vaguest suggestion of a shape in the midst of a dim light, but it is evolving quickly. It is clearly floating, yet the shape is now human-like! There is a swirl and a flurry of a crimson cloak. The light brightens to blinding brilliance. In this rectangle of light, framed by Red Rogan's gravestone, a ghost comes into sharp focus.

Terrified, Richelle steps backwards. She stumbles over a crumbling headstone and lands heavily on her back. All her breath is knocked out of her. The ghost floats forward, bending so that it is right over her.

'No no no!' she gasps. The ghost's face is almost touching hers. Ready to seal their meeting with a kiss . . .

THREE

Springtime in Spring Street, Melbourne. There is a spring in the Mythbusters' steps, too. The skyline is like that in many other modern cities, crowded with competing monstrosities of concrete and glass. But the place also has charm. Tree-lined boulevards, lush parklands, impressive old churches and banks. The three million people live in the flat surrounding suburbs which spread out almost as far as the distant blue hills of the Dandenongs.

Bowvayne, Strange and Digweed walk past the imposing Parliament House, cross Spring Street and see the famous Princess Theatre for the first time. 'Magnificent,' Bowvayne mutters to himself. It is crowned with three great turrets, golden lions and a golden angelic trumpeter which gazes down benignly from on high, and on either side are stone Grecian urns.

They pass beneath the copper awning and enter the theatre. On their right is an impressive colonnade that leads to the auditorium. But they turn left and head straight for the Federici Bar, named after a famous phantom who is said to haunt the theatre. Bowvayne smiles wryly when he sees that *Phantom of the Opera* is the current show.

Digweed says with a crooked grin, 'There's a couple more spirits here than in most bars!' They struggle through the crowd to buy drinks, then seat themselves at a small table. Bowvayne and Digweed sip beers. Strange has something that looks more like a tropical island than a drink, complete with plastic palm-trees, monkeys, fruit and a blue lagoon. They are waiting for Matthew Mann, a friend of Richelle Le Saux's parents who is quite naturally worried for her and also wishes to warn the Mythbusters that they're tampering with dark forces.

Eventually, a bespectacled scarecrow of a man introduces himself. He is perhaps forty, wearing a crumpled brown suit that hangs from his scrawny frame. 'Mythbusters?'

'Busting to bust!' Digweed says grandly. 'Pleased to meet you, Mr Mann.'

Mann buys himself a coffee and sits at the Mythbusters' table. The bar is filled with a noisy hubbub and everyone needs to talk loudly.

'We're really hoping you've got some information to help our investigation,' says Strange, taking a mini-recorder from the breast pocket of his shirt.

'I'm not sure I'm doing you any favours giving you more information. You're all young fools — yourselves and Richelle — for delving into these ancient secrets, this ancient curse. No good will come of it, of that I'm sure,' he adds ominously. Mann sips his drink, and the brown skin that has formed on top of the coffee transfers itself to his front teeth.

Bowvayne, as is his wont, brightens up at the sound of curses and considerable danger. 'But how do you know so much about Red Rogan, Mr Mann?'

'Richelle's mother and I have been friends for more than twenty-five years. We were younger than Richelle when we too were drawn by the ghostly tale of the graveyard. It seemed an exciting thing to do at the time. But it soon turned into a terrrifying ordeal . . .

'I remember it was just after dusk that we caught a momentary flash of a red cloak. Legend tells that Red Rogan always wears such a garment. And the sighting was close to his grave.

'But that was just the start of it. When we went to his actual gravestone, a handsome gypsy in red was waiting for us. Quite normal he looked apart from the fact that we could see straight through him. And there was a look of interminable misery and sadness on his face. I'm not ashamed to say we ran for our lives.

48

'Wanting to get to the bottom of the mystery, Richelle's mother and I did extensive research. And that led to the most amazing discovery of all. For while looking into the family history, we came across the birth certificate of Marie Le Saux's son, George. He was born in 1890 with her maiden name, Pierrot. She must have been unmarried when George came into the world. George's father's name was on the paper too. The name was — Ricard Rogan!'

The three Mythbusters gasp in amazement. Then everyone shouts at once.

'So he wants revenge!' yells Digweed.

'So Marie must have married Jacques Le Saux for money and to save her honour!' yells Strange.

'So Rogan's obsessed with the Le Saux descendants, as they are all his. The same old story when it comes to ghosts, full of deceit and betrayal!' yells Bowvayne.

But Bowvayne is still puzzled. 'What I don't understand is that Red Rogan had his revenge. In the fight between them, Le Saux died by Rogan's hand, and then he reclaimed Marie with his kiss of death. Strange discovered all this more than a week ago. So why does he still haunt the Melbourne Cemetery?'

Mann looks almost ghoulish. 'He has the woman he loved with him. Now he wants the rest of his family!'

Strange shudders. 'I'm worried for Richelle. She's the one in most danger. She shouldn't keep going there.' How eerily portentous those words prove to be . . .

'One more question,' mumbles Digweed. 'I was . . . er . . . wondering why you asked to meet us here, at the Princess Theatre?'

Mann smiles, his mouth all brown and gooey with the coffee-skin. 'Good question. I thought it fitting as this is the place where Marie and Red Rogan met, all those years ago. He was a stage-hand and she was a dancing girl here.'

'Hmm,' Bowvayne muses. 'So much to consider. Wherever will we start?'

FOUR

Back at Mythbase (Oz)-1, the Mythbusters are chewing their way through one of Strange's famous home-made soups. Bowvayne and Digweed push their bowls away when they can eat no more. 'I feel like a beached walrus,' Bowvayne groans, putting his feet up on the glass-topped table.

Strange is still going strong, the spoon moving in a blur of silver. This is punctuated intermittently with ecstatic moaning noises. The telephone hotline interrupts this gluttonous frenzy.

Strange waddles over to the phone, bowl in hand. 'Ah, Richelle. I've been trying to contact you for days. How are you, my dear? I heard you had a terrible fright.' Strange puts his hand over the mouthpiece and whispers to the others, 'It's Richelle. I've been trying to contact her for days. She's fine. She's had a terrible fright.'

'Really?' Bowvayne says dryly.

Strange goes back to her. '. . . You've been to the cemetery again . . . Swirl of a red cloak again . . . Didn't kiss you, thank goodness! . . . Psychic inkling . . . Bag of cashews . . . Yes, we can . . . Tonight . . . Strange powers . . .' Strange powers another spoonful of soup into his mouth. 'Yes, we can meet you there . . . Fine . . .'

*

9 p.m. An alarm clock rings. The trio scurry to the Equipment Room. They jump into their black overalls and strap belts with tape-recorders attached – called Sound Belts – round their waists. After putting on backpacks and fastening down one another's miners' hard hats, they check and double-check their IRKs. IRK stands for Infra-Red Kirlian, an advanced movie-camera designed to film, even in total darkness, visitors from the spirit world. They're ready!

The Mythbusters leave the office and clamber into the Mythrover. The mixed aroma of blossom, carbon monoxide and the nearby Pizza Palace Home Delivery Service assaults their nostrils. They sneeze simultaneously.

'Damned hay fever,' says Bowvayne.

'Damned car fumes,' says Strange.

'Damned garlic,' says Digweed.

The Mythrover gives a bang-putt-pharrrt and lurches forward. Melbourne Cemetery, here they come!

The cemetery is a huge, sprawling place; easily a kilometre square of gently undulating ground, long grass where cicadas chirrup shrilly and tall thin eucalypts sway in the breeze. Stark, silver and sinister in the moonlight, gravestones of granite and marble seem to sprout up ever more quickly, the longer the Mythbusters stare, hundreds and hundreds of them, as far as the eye can see. The dead are of many different religions, not just Christian, and the epitaphs in many different languages.

Barring their way in is a three-metre-high wrought-iron fence, a spear-shaped adornment at the top of each bar. The gates have been locked since dusk at six o'clock. As if the wrought-iron fence wasn't enough protection, great loops of barbed wire are also tangled along the top. Strange shudders.

Studying the awesome fortifications, Bowvayne looks for a weak point. 'Do you think they're trying to keep the dead in or the living out?'

Digweed chuckles good-naturedly.

'Th-that's not f-funny, Bow,' Strange says, scowling. 'Anyway, I envisaged this problem. That's why there's a ladder in the back of the Mythrover.'

The Mythbusters scuttle back to the vehicle. Strange is more jumpy than a frog contemplating a nap in France.

Bowvayne looks at his watch. 'Richelle is late. We'll give her fifteen minutes.'

9.30 p.m. Still no sign of Richelle. They climb the ladder, leap into the dark unknown on the other side and land awkwardly on solid concrete. After a few groans and some rubbing of sore ankles, they get their bearings, pull the ladder over with them and hide it in some bushes. They pick their way through ancient, crumbling monuments and smashed ruins among overgrown weeds. A bitumen path is just ahead.

'Due north,' whimpers Strange as they trudge onward. Then, more fussily, 'You do realize that if we're caught in here we'll probably be jailed for grave-robbing or something.'

Bowvayne grins. 'Grave-robber. That would look pretty bad on the passports!'

The moon disappears behind dark, scurrying clouds. Now the night is as black as the inside of a coffin.

Bowvayne halts. 'Let's get out our goggles. We never know what we're going to find – and I want to be ready.'

Digweed nods. 'Good idea.'

They take pairs of infra-red goggles from each other's backpacks. As Bowvayne starts groping around in Strange's pack, he suddenly looks at him accusingly. 'You've got a flask of vegetable soup in here! No wonder you were complaining about the backpack being heavy.'

'Emergency rations,' Strange says sheepishly.

They put on their infra-red goggles. Digweed scans over a tree, to see honey-eaters sleeping, heads snuggled under wings.

The Mythbusters look ridiculous, like deep-sea fish with flickering filaments for eyes. But they don't care. How exciting to see so perfectly in this complete blackness – invaders of the night world with their invisible light! On and on they go, fresh secrets and experiences revealed with every step in this dark world.

Strange looks around. 'Not far from Red Rogan's grave now.'

The inscription on the tombstone is now pale and weathered: a small monument to a man's life. They stare at it, caught in personal reveries.

Bowvayne shudders, then breaks the silence. 'I feel as if someone's walking on my grave.'

'Don't say that here,' begs Strange, beads of sweat forming on his forehead.

'But he's right,' Digweed says to Strange. 'I feel as though someone's watching me.'

There's a noise like a cry. The Mythbusters freeze.

Something appears from behind the grave. A shadow rising up from the earth! Looming before them!

'Hi, it's Richelle Le Saux. You guys are late . . .' she calls after three figures that are running away so fast you can't see them for dust.

FIVE

Four people walk out of the Mythbusters' office to the Mythrover. One is a girl in her teens. She is slim and petite with honey-blonde hair, and her large green eyes have something bewitching about them. With her are three characters who look as if they might be pest exterminators . . . or just mad.

They are Richelle Le Saux and the Mythbusters. Two weeks have passed since their little misunderstanding in the cemetery. Strange is beginning to wonder whether all the stories about Red Rogan are just hysterical nonsense. Maybe he is mad to believe a word Richelle says.

Bowvayne is his normal self; he'll believe anything once. He is trying to tackle the problem of their shy spook in an organized way. 'How did you escape Rogan's deadly kiss? Maybe that could give us a clue to finding him.'

Her voice is a breathless whisper. 'Ooh, it was just horrible. After I'd stumbled backwards over that headstone, Red Rogan's swarthy face drifted down almost to mine. I screamed, I think, and turned my torch on to full beam. I don't know what happened to him after I rolled out of the way, but he was gone. Lucky.'

Bowvayne nods, satisfied. 'So this ghost reacts to strong light. It's torches off from now on. We don't want to scare him away.'

'Don't we?' Digweed gulps, then lapses back into nervous silence.

Bowvayne adds smoothly, 'You're pretty brave to still be coming with us after what happened, Richelle.'

She smiles wanly. 'Look, I've been thinking,' she begins, swallowing her fear. 'Red Rogan's probably not going to harm me since, according to you guys, I'm his great-granddaughter. I'll go to him as I did before, try to make contact, tell him to Rest In Peace and all that. You can all . . .'

'Far too dangerous. We can't allow it. Don't say another word,' interrupts Strange.

'. . . hide near by and capture it on film with your IRKs. If anything goes wrong, you'll be ready to dazzle him with your torches.'

'Great plan! Let's go!' Bowvayne says unchivalrously.

'I may as well speak to myself,' Strange speaks to himself.

Midnight. There is a hint of rain in the cool night air. The foursome have just scaled Melbourne Cemetery's fence again. And it's darker than the underside of a bat's wing in there without their torches.

Digweed stands rigid and tense, like an animal sensing danger. 'Right,' Bowvayne says finally. 'Let's split up into pairs. Chris, you and Diggers go straight to the grave.

Richelle and I will skirt around the perimeter for a bit and approach Red Rogan's grave from the opposite direction. This will give us a chance to find a hiding place and be ready with the IRKs. If things get out of hand for you, we'll turn on our torches to scare him off.'

Frowning enviously, Strange watches Bowvayne disappear into the darkness with Richelle.

Bowvayne and Richelle follow the line of the fence. Then they head into the middle of the cemetery, towards Red Rogan's burial-place. They hop gingerly over an antique vault and pick their way carefully through an obstacle course of newer marble gravestones.

The wind picks up. The hint of rain becomes a torrent, hissing harshly as it strikes the smashed ruins and tall weeds. The pair dash under a small clump of trees to escape the downpour.

Richelle squints at her map. 'We're pretty close now.' But they stay under cover for five minutes or more.

Bowvayne points up ahead. Through his infra-red goggles he can see a tiny flickering rectangle of light in the distance. Emanating from Red Rogan's grave . . .

Richelle hurries Bowvayne forward. 'Quick! It's just like last time!'

'Let's hope Diggers and Chris are ready,' Bowvayne says worriedly.

Closer. Closer . . . They are oblivious to the fact that they're getting soaked. Now they can see his gravestone. Yes, there's that psychic inkling again, Richelle thinks.

There is a crimson tinge to the wind. A moment of intense cold. The rain eases.

Then . . .

. . . Searing white light explodes from Rogan's head-

56

stone. With a twirling flourish of his cloak, what must be the gypsy ghost is standing in front of them.

He sees Richelle first. When he looks at Bowvayne, Red Rogan's face twists in jealous rage.

'I think you'd better get out of here,' Richelle hisses.

But Bowvayne is transfixed. He wants to run away but can't, like a rabbit hypnotized by a car's headlights.

Six

'Get out of here!' she begs him now. This ghost is turning decidedly nasty with Bowvayne around.

The Mythbuster gulps. Then he addresses the ghost as if Red Rogan was the boxing champion father of his girlfriend. 'We're just good friends – honest!' His eyes grow wide with terror.

Because apparently Rogan doesn't see it that way. The handsome gypsy face fades – replaced by a foul and wormy skull. The remaining flaps of skin are cankered and decayed.

Without warning, a bony arm reaches out for the Mythbuster, its skeletal fingers click-clacking as they close on nothing. In that split-second Bowvayne hurls himself sideways and backwards, out of reach of the claw of death. 'Turn on the torches! Chris! Diggers!'

No answer.

With a horrifying shriek, the skeleton floats towards him. Desperation grips Bowvayne. He fumbles with his torch. Drops it. It rolls away into the darkness. His last hope gone. Red Rogan's bones loom ever closer, closer to Bowvayne's face. Oh no, not the kiss!

Richelle shouts with great authority, 'Ricard Rogan! Be at peace. We understand why you haunt this place. And I know I am your great-granddaughter . . .'

At that moment Red Rogan becomes whole again. His handsome gypsy face reappears — and he turns to Richelle and smiles.

Then there is a blinding wall of light.

Confusion. Bowvayne runs one way and Richelle another. Strange and Digweed come out of the darkness holding torches.

'Is everything all right?'

'What happened?'

'The ghost! The ghost! Red Rogan is here! Did you film it on the IRKs?' Bowvayne implores, not unhysterically.

Digweed is dreadfully disappointed. 'We took shelter from the rain. We didn't see a thing.'

'We didn't think you'd even be here yet!' curses Strange, wild with frustration.

'Let's scout around now; we might still find him,' Digweed says resolutely. The others agree.

'Did anything much happen?' Strange asks Bowvayne and Richelle.

Bowvayne replies with heavy irony, 'You might say that.'

But they search in vain. Red Rogan has gone.

Artist's impression of Red Rogan's ghost

CASE CLOSING NOTES

Peter Underwood, president of the Ghost Club Society, wrote, 'I have investigated thousands of reported hauntings, of which I am convinced hundreds are genuine. I believe that ghosts exist, although I have not seen one myself – there is too much evidence for them all to be manufactured.'

The Mythbusters expect everyone reading this knows someone who claims to have seen a ghost. Surely with so many sightings there should be little doubt that they actually exist. But there is doubt. Why?

The answer to this lies in the very nature of the spirit world. They are 'borderline' entities: existing on the line between reality and fantasy. Sanity and madness. Life and death. Who can speak with conviction of things that dwell in these realms?

But why should ghosts trespass back to this world, where they no longer belong? For many reasons. A lover has betrayed them. A false friend has murdered them. They were cheated out of completing a work of great importance by Death. People who lead normal lives seldom return as ghosts (unless danger threatens a loved-one still living). But it is those who feel cheated or betrayed that are the largest percentage of the ones who 'come back'.

And Red Rogan? He felt cheated, of course. He was

cheated of the woman he loved, a happy family and, ultimately, his life by circumstance. He had no money. Money *might* have brought him happiness. Jacques Le Saux had money. So he won Marie, little George, everything. Rogan's frustration lived on even after he and Le Saux had fought to the death. But now, a hundred years later, Richelle Le Saux has let him know they recognize him as blood-kin. Red Rogan will Rest in Peace.

We hope.

3. Bunyips and Big Cats

MYTHBUSTERS CASE FILE

TITLE: Bunyips and Big Cats

CODE: 001Oz 170891

LOCATION: Australia's Little Desert
                     stretches from the Wimmera
                     River to the South Australian
                     border, and is half-way
                     between the cities of
                     Melbourne and Adelaide

MYTHBUSTERS: Bowvayne
                     Chris Strange

TERRAIN: Aeolian dunes and sand sheets
                     blanket much of this semi-arid
                     area of north-western Victoria.
                     Occasional sandstone ridges
                     and higher sandhills. It has an
                     abundance of wildlife and is
                     quite densely vegetated. The
                     tracks are very sandy and
                     suitable for four-wheel-drive
                     vehicles only

DIFFICULTIES: Searing temperatures that can reach 43°C. Sudden temperature changes. Deadly snakes and other dangerous animals. Some almost impenetrable areas to traverse

MISSION: Full-scale investigation. Attempt to capture these twin phenomena on film, discovering whether the mythical bunyip really does exist and whether big cats live in this Australian desert

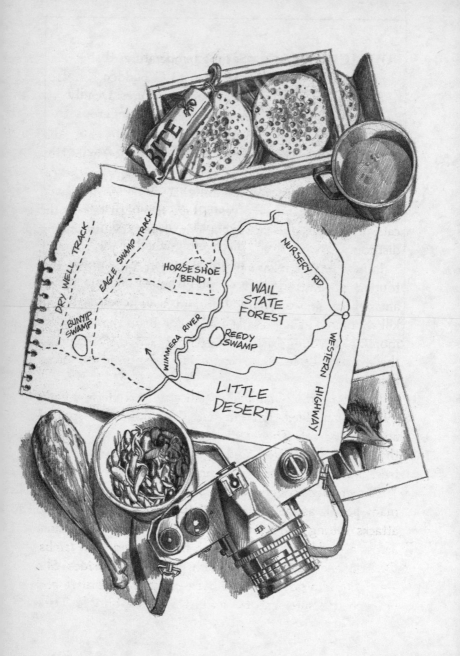

CASE HISTORY

The most important fact regarding 'big cats' is this: Australia shouldn't have any; it is a country dominated by marsupials. There are no indigenous members of the cat species, nor official recognition that any cats live wild in Australia. Yet for fifty years there has been talk of the cats' mysterious presence in the Wimmera and surrounding districts.

In July 1991, adventurer 'Tricky' Dicky Sidebottom was touring the Little Desert in a friend's jeep when, to his amazement, he watched a 'simply massive beast' stalk and kill an injured kangaroo. At Horseshoe Bend the following morning, a young Irish woman, Polly Waddle, unzipping the exit-flap of her tent, was sure she spotted the same animal.

In the nearby Grampians National Park during early 1987, Jillian Read, Jim Pitt and Gary Johnston spotted another big cat. They said the beast's head was bigger than a man's. Johnston studied it as it sat in the fork of a tree, and it met his gaze with clear, green-yellow eyes.

Farmer Hec Rogers, who lives in the area known by many people as the 'big cat belt', lost four sheep in horrific attacks during 1978. He said: 'One night ... we came across a freshly killed ewe which had just had twin lambs. One rib had been torn out with part of her insides. She was lying in a pool of blood but her lambs were alive and untouched, a sure sign that a fox wasn't responsible. They always go for the lamb.'

He added, 'The animal eats all the hind leg, right to the backbone. It must be big because of the amount it eats at each kill.'

The numerous big cat sightings seem to date all the way back to the Second World War.

In Australian mythology, the bunyip is a man-eating water monster which lurks in the mud at the bottom of swamps and lakes. Aborigines claim that for thousands of years they have been falling prey to this terrifying creature. Cynics scoff at the bunyip, pointing out that no one *really* knows what it looks like. One local sheep farmer said: 'I'd believe in flying pink elephants in bikinis before I believed in bunyips in the Little Desert!'

Young Aborigine Jimmy Zak from neighbouring Horsham says the cynics have missed the point. 'If you were walking across the desert and saw a Tyrannosaurus Rex, the chances are you wouldn't live to tell the tale. He'd gobble you up! It's the same story with the bunyip.'

Jimmy Zak told the Mythbusters that his uncle had spotted the mythological monster at the aptly named Bunyip Swamp (known officially as Eagle Swamp) in the Little Desert some years before . . . and had lived to tell the tale! He had been sheltering from a heavy downpour of rain in a clump of trees, when the bunyip rose from the water in front of him. Unfortunately, this eye-witness refused to be interviewed by Mythbusters, fearing ridicule from his friends.

But Jimmy's second-hand description is of an awesome, long-necked reptile with a mighty, beak-like head, armoured scales, switchblade-like claws and a club-type tail.

Apparently the man's hair turned completely white after this brief, nightmarish encounter.

The bunyip is said to make a loud booming roar, particularly during or after long rainy spells, but never during a drought. When the swamps and lakes dry up, the bunyip hibernates by burrowing deep into the mud.

ONE

The Little Desert stretches from the Wimmera River to the South Australian border, and is halfway between the cities of Melbourne and Adelaide. It isn't really a desert — well, not a proper one anyway. Although rich in desert features, sand dunes and sandstone ridges, parts of it are densely vegetated and others are quite swampy. In the springtime some areas are ablaze with colour from a huge variety of wild flowers. The Little Desert's temperature can be cruelly hot; and its giant emu birds, second in size only to the ostrich, have been known cruelly to steal mixed bean salad breakfasts from sleeping campers.

The Mythrover pulls up at Horseshoe Bend. Surrounded by heathlands of banksia, tea-tree and drooping she-oak, it is a wonderful section of the Wimmera River. On the very edge of the Little Desert, the majestic, ghost-like gum-trees are mirror-reflected in the graceful, sinuous water.

A somewhat less graceful and sinuous Chris Strange swings open the creaking driver's door of the Mythrover. He is clearly hot because of the desert, tired because of the long drive from Mythbase (Oz)-1, and irritable because of Bowvayne's deranged exuberance.

Strange glances at his fellow Mythbuster in the passenger seat, closes his eyes determinedly and says in a tone that brooks no argument, 'Right, this is what's going to happen, mate. We're going to do things in an orderly, organized fashion. First, we'll check the equipment list and make sure every item is present and fit for duty. And I mean check *everything*. Down to the last screw, bolt, battery and paper-clip. Then we'll pitch the tent, *before* it gets dark this time. I suggest we pitch it in three separate spots before deciding which one is best. All this'll only take three or four hours. I know it won't be fun, but by then we'll have a serious appetite and I'll make some garlic mushroom parcels with cumquat juice.

'You've got to admit, my way's the most sensible way of doing things, mate. With you it's all waving your arms about and getting us side-tracked and involving us in lunatic activities that usually end in chaos and confusion and . . . Bow? Bowvayne!'

Bowvayne is up to his chest in a small swamp, a few metres away. 'Quick! Quick!' he yells, waving his arms about excitedly. 'Bring the nets and jars. I've just found some fantastic giant white tadpoles! We've got to catch some!'

If the ancient and wise Methuselah had had to babysit for an overexcited young chimpanzee, his exasperated sigh wouldn't have matched Strange's at this moment.

TWO

Seven o'clock next morning. Bowvayne is shocked from sleep by an eye-boggling screech of utter desolation and indescribable torment. My God, he thinks as he scrambles from his sleeping-bag and out of the two-man-Mythtent, it's not the bunyip already, is it? Panic mounting, it dawns on him that Strange is not in the tent and he's nowhere in sight. Devoured by the monster . . .?

In the distance he can hear an odd drumming sound that fools his ears into thinking it's coming from all directions at once. It is the sound of a female emu. This is followed by a high-pitched, strangled voice. 'Maaaaa . . . maaaaa . . . maaaaayt.'

Suddenly, out of the heather, a flock of flightless but fleet-footed emu, some almost two metres tall, come stampeding into view. Bowvayne backs off against the tent as they pass him. His fellow Mythbuster is staggering exhaustedly in pursuit of the last emu, which is holding in its beak one of Strange's beloved plastic lunchboxes. Bowvayne roars with laughter at the mad scene before him; the beanbox swinging backwards and forwards by its handle in the escaping bird's beak, and Strange screeching in utter desolation and indescribable torment, 'Mate! Mate! Mate! The emus have taken all the mixed bean salad! The emus have taken all the mixed bean salad! Stop that one, mate! Stop, thief! Stop, thief!'

Feeling sorry for his friend, a still-grinning Bowvayne chases the bird, only hoping that the lunchbox will be dropped. There's no way he's going to attempt to catch it, knowing that an emu's kick can be fatal. But with great powerful strides, the emu with the beans accelerates to nearly fifty kilometres an hour, and soon all Bowvayne can see is its fluffy, straw-like tail disappearing into the scrub.

He joins a disconsolate, mixed bean saladless Strange, who is slumped on the sand. 'Come on, Chris. We've got some bunyips and big cats to find.'

Soon the Mythrover is labouring up its first sand dune, the engine screaming as the wheels sink dangerously deeper and deeper. All around is banksia heathland, whose large fluffy nuts carpet the ground, waiting for a bushfire so they can germinate. Strange changes gear down into first. The tyres find extra 'bite' in the ever-shifting sand; his foot pushes the accelerator pedal to the floor, and finally they struggle to the top. Strange dabs his sweaty forehead with a handkerchief. 'I hope it's not all going to be like that. We almost got stuck there.'

In the passenger seat Bowvayne studies the Little Desert map and says carelessly, 'By my reckoning there's only another two hundred dunes like that to climb today!'

Stretching out before them is the most extraordinary scene. The pair jump out of the Mythrover, cameras and mini-recorders in their hands. A great, boundless, deep-blue sky seems so close to their heads, the Mythbusters think they can almost touch it. And the sun seems bigger and hotter and nearer somehow, like a cruel yellow eye staring into them. A line of sand dunes waits for them, the farthest one a dot in the heat-shimmering distance. From the scrub on either side big grey kangaroos study the Mythrover curiously. A baby kangaroo, known as a joey, pops its head out of its mother's pouch and its lovely brown eyes gaze at Bowvayne. A flock of sulphur-crested cockatoos wheels overhead, screeching raucously. Emus parade across the dune in front of the Mythbusters, presumably hoping for more mixed bean salad.

'I'll make you into emu kebabs!' Strange threatens them. Then he remembers that his investigation mini-recorder is still recording. He chuckles. 'I'd better erase that bit later.'

Late morning. The Mythrover is bouncing along tortuous trails in the heart of the Little Desert. It is very hot now. 'We're about to reach the Mallee Track, I think.

Sidebottom saw his big cat around here somewhere,' Bowvayne says, poring over the map.

The vehicle lurches into a particularly wide, sun-dried crack, and the Mythbusters' heads smash against the roof. 'Right, enough's enough,' Strange snaps irritably. 'I'm getting out for lunch — and for breakfast too. I haven't even had that yet.' In front is a series of red-gum-crowned hills, like shaded island sanctuaries in this sea of sand.

Steam billows from the Mythrover as it finally grinds to a halt in the comparative coolness of the first red-gum rise. Steam billows from Strange as he lovingly spreads out his picnic blanket on which are depicted penguins, polar bears and wintry scenes, of all things! Bowvayne watches, open-mouthed, as Strange lights the little portable gas-stove, boils a pan of water and makes himself a piping-hot mug of tea, and then . . . spears crumpets with a long brass toasting-fork and, using the flickering blue flame, toasts one piping-hot crumpet after another piping-hot crumpet for himself.

Bowvayne just eats an entire water melon.

There is a furtive movement behind them. A rather drab-looking bird that just might be a cross between a chicken and a pigeon scurries away into the scrub. Bowvayne follows, absolutely fascinated. For this is the elusive malleefowl. Near by, the bird has built a marvellous pyramid of sand, easily three metres across. The core of the pyramid is rotting vegetation and, carefully placed in this and forming a circle, are its eggs. Every so often the male malleefowl probes his rather splendid 'compost heap' nest with his tongue, making sure that the fermenting matter is at the perfect temperature for his offspring to hatch. The bird soon spots Bowvayne and bobs away, making a sound like water gurgling through old pipes.

Strange has finished his second packet of crumpets and is looking full and content when Bowvayne returns. 'Right, to the Mythrover, mate. I'm ready to face anything now. The only thing that'll stop me finding a big cat is being waylaid by a bunyip!'

Thank goodness he's forgotten about his mixed bean salad, Bowvayne thinks.

'Shame about the mixed bean salad, though,' Strange adds. Bowvayne rolls his eyes.

They bump bump their way along Dahlenburgs Mill Track, never going at more than twenty-five kph or higher than second gear. On either side is relatively flat scrubland that slopes gently downwards. Vividly coloured blue wrens dart across the track in front of them. After half an hour of this, Strange spots a small, almost dried-up swamp.

'It's not on my map. Let's go and investigate,' says Bowvayne.

'Yeah, good idea.'

Swinging open the doors of the Mythrover and letting the desert in is like opening an oven door. The surge of heat is dizzying in its intensity. Even wearing sunglasses, the pair have to shield their eyes against the fierce glare as they jump lightly on to the sand. The Mythbusters walk slowly through the scrub — deadly snakes are a real danger here — to what turns out to be no more than a muddy water-hole.

They squat down on their haunches beside it to rest for a moment. 'Hey! Look at these!' Bowvayne yells suddenly. 'Pawprints!'

Strange nods enthusiastically. 'Pawprints of a big cat!'

THREE

The Mythrover labours up another daunting desert dune, the sand under its rear tyres being spat out backwards. Strange is hunched over the steering-wheel, his brow furrowed in concentration. 'Come on, old girl, you can do it,' he coaxes as the engine squeals with the exertion. 'Come on. Come on.' The situation looks serious.

Without warning, Bowvayne suddenly slaps his friend's face. 'You had a mosquito on you,' he explains quickly, seeing Strange's outraged expression.

'Did you get it?'

'Yes,' Bowvayne lies.

The frazzled driver applies R.I.D. roll-on insect repellent to his furrowed brow, whiskery cheeks and sun-reddened nose.

It is a week later. They have had no sightings — not even any further clues — of big cats, let alone of bunyips. And, even worse, thinks Strange, dinner was a thoroughly unsatisfying affair, one measly potato pancake each. Food supplies are running low.

Bowvayne splatters on his own forearm a mosquito that had seemed intent on draining every drop of his life's blood. 'My God! These mosquitoes are the size of dinner plates!'

'And our dinners are the size of mosquitoes' plates,' Strange responds dryly.

The Mythrover battles valiantly to the top of the dune. 'Oh, go on, let me drive, now we've made it up here,' Bowvayne whines, not for the first time today.

This gives Strange another opportunity to be the 'wise old owl'. 'Listen, mate, this stretch of desert is far too difficult. You know how hot-headed and irresponsible you are. You're not like me. I've got ice running through my veins, the sharp eye of an eagle, the driving skills of a Grand Prix racer, the reflexes of a . . . well, of a thing with fast reflexes and . . .'

Bowvayne has a crafty look in his eye. 'If you let me drive, I'll give you my Mars bar.'

'It's a deal!'

Seconds later, Bowvayne is grinning victoriously in the driver's seat, pretending to listen to his fellow Myth-buster's half-hour education course on 'How to Drive the Mythrover'. Strange is sucking a very melted piece of chocolate at the same time.

The Mythrover trundles down the great sand dune. Fifteen kilometres an hour. Twenty-five. The vehicle begins to gather momentum. Thirty. Forty. Forty-five.

'Too fast! Too fast! Slow it down!' Strange says with authority. 'Get it back down to twenty-five.'

The rebellious 'Toad of Toad Hall' aspect of Bowvayne's personality surfaces. The speedometer's needle steadfastly sticks on forty kph. So delighted is he finally to be at the wheel of one of the Mythvehicles that he sounds the horn and bursts into song:

> 'The motor-car went *Poop-poop-poop*,
> As it raced along the road.
> Who was it steered it into a pond?
> Ingenious Mr Toad!'

Strange snaps, 'Twenty-five, mate. Get the speed down to Twenty-five.'

Sulkily, Bowvayne obeys.

Disaster strikes with shocking suddenness.

As they round a tree-shaded corner, the Mythrover
runs over what looks like a piece of long, thick, brown
rope. The front wheel flicks it into the air, and the brown
'rope' lands with a thud on the windscreen. Bowvayne and
Strange are staring straight into the cruel eyes of one of
the world's most poisonous snakes: the brown snake.

The crippled creature lunges viciously at them, spraying
poison across the windscreen.

Instinctively, Bowvayne ducks, and he loses control of
the Mythrover. It lurches violently into a tree. There is an
awful sound of splintering wood and twisting of metal. A
hiss of steam.

Then . . .

. . . nothing.

FOUR

The Mythbusters drift back into consciousness, clutching
their pounding heads gingerly.

'Are you all right, mate?' Strange asks. He has a slight
cut on his left cheek.

Bowvayne rubs his eyes absently. 'Yeah, just about.'

The Mythrover is swaying from side to side in a slow,
rhythmical fashion. Like it's afloat at sea. Immediately in
front of them the stringybark tree doesn't move.

'You mustn't blame yourself for what happened. There
was nothing you could have done,' Strange says charitably.
'That could've happened to anyone.'

78

'When that snake struck out at us, for that split-second I just forgot the windscreen was between us and it.' The vehicle leans alarmingly to one side. 'Hey! Why is the Mythrover wobbling about?'

But Strange acknowledges neither the question nor the wobbling. 'I'm just glad the Mythrover has such a strong bumper bar . . . ar . . . ar . . . Ah! Ah! Ah! Ah! Ah!' He slaps at his own legs wildly.

Great copper and yellow ants this big are swarming all over the interior of the car; every second, thousands more are pouring through the gaps in the frames of the doors, the air-coolers and any other available crevice.

There are so many ants on Bowvayne's feet, he can't see his running shoes. He screams. Over and over again. Their bites are extremely painful, like slamming a door shut and leaving a finger there. Over and over again.

Fearful of being eaten alive – and having ant-filled pants besides – the Mythbusters swing open their doors, disturbing mounds of sand. This is definitely a mistake. Armies more ants invade. The whole scene is a seething mass of copper and yellow.

The pair have to abandon the car. But to where? The ground, inexplicably a metre or so below them, is also swarming with ants. They exit at speed and clamber up on to the Mythrover's roof.

'They're anti us,' Strange quips, scratching his stinging legs.

'Ha ha,' says Bowvayne. Then he shakes his head in mock disappointment. 'There's never an anteater around when you need one.'

The Mythbusters peer over the side, holding on to the

metal rail of the roof-rack. The old Land Rover is astride two demolished anthills; the monuments, once two metres high, are now half that and are a chaotic scene of labyrinthine tunnels and feverish insect activity.

'It looks like we disturbed a couple of ants' nests,' Strange says rather unnecessarily.

Bowvayne is about to make a sarcastic rejoinder when the Mythrover teeters dramatically, preparing to roll over and crash on to its side. 'It's our extra weight that's pushing it over!' he wails. 'Across to the other side and make a jump for it. Quick!'

The pair go clattering earthwards, and find themselves sprawling on the sandy track, just out of the ants' reach. They watch with relief as the Mythrover, silhouetted against a pink sunset, regains its equilibrium.

In the desert the night arrives very suddenly, and it is soon as black as the bottom of a well full of ink. The Mythtent, the food, drink, torches, insect-bite creams and a dozen other essentials are all in the car. Which is doubtless still full of unwanted guests. Waiting to bite them again.

And it's a dangerous business sleeping on the ground when you are out in the wild. You never know what might be creeping about. Or what might think nothing of stinging you, biting you or sucking your blood.

So the Mythbusters spend a miserable night dozing fitfully up in a tree.

FIVE

Clearing the Mythrover of its ant occupants next morning is a tedious, time-consuming and tricky task, finally achieved by painstakingly covering every centimetre of the interior with insect spray and swatting survivors with rolled-up newspapers. Then every item in the car is carefully removed and brushed clean of ants. Once this is done, the vehicle makes a hasty, bumpy 'reverse' off the ant mounds and trundles to Bunyip Swamp, Strange now back in the driver's seat. The damaged Mythrover makes protesting 'hisses' and rattles all the way.

The Mythbusters find the whole of Bunyip Swamp dried out when they jump from the car and stand at the swamp's edge. It is a stark yet beautiful scene before them: the 'swamp', at least half a kilometre across in any direction, is now a mosaic floor of sun-cracked mud. There are embedded emu tracks receding into the distance, spoiling the mosaic's symmetry somewhat. Around the rim of the swamp the banks rise steeply to where tall eucalypts grow. Pink galahs and the snake-hunting kookaburra bird are perched in them.

Strange takes a deep breath, as if he's inhaling Paradise itself. 'We'll camp here, it's so so peaceful.' A galah makes an amazingly raucous double-screech. Strange frowns, his paradise shattered.

'Some creatures just don't appreciate Nature,' Bowvayne says.

The temperature in the shade is about 39°C. After pitching the Mythtent Strange performs some minor repairs on the car. Bowvayne has found something he calls his bunyip-stick, a large corkscrew-shaped eucalyptus branch the same height as him, and he is probing deeper and deeper below the mosaic floor for bunyips! About ten centimetres under the surface the mud is wet and gooey; the sort of 'goo' people might pay a fortune for if it were sold in a fancy jar in a smart department store and called 'Amazonia's Anti-Ageing Mud Pack'. 'If we can't find a big cat, then I'm going to find a bunyip,' he mutters determinedly.

Strange wanders over to join his friend, pulling a broad-brimmed hat down tightly over his forehead, shielding him from the harsh glare. 'I've got to go into Dimboola for food supplies, mate. Or it's grubs and treebark for dinner tonight. And the milk looks more like lumpy melted cheese, and the smell . . .'

Bowvayne holds a hand up. 'All right! All right! Spare me the details. I'll stay here and keep watch for bunyips and big cats.'

'It's two o'clock now. I'll be back before seven.'

After the Mythrover has gone, Bowvayne soon tires of using the bunyip-stick in a fruitless search for clues, and decides to scour the tree-shaded banks instead. A kookaburra flaps lazily from tree to tree as Bowvayne scrambles up a bank and enters the relative cool. Twigs snap beneath his feet and beetles of various colours scurry about in front of him. He treads carefully, wary of snakes. A basking snake can look just like a dead branch . . . that is, until you tread on it and it buries its poison-filled fangs in your leg . . .

Suddenly he hears a growl. A long, rumbling growl. Bowvayne whirls around, wondering what has caused the sound. Where has it come from? 'Keep calm. Keep calm,' he mutters to himself. Then there's another long, rumbling growl. Closer this time. Just ahead of him. The Mythbuster pauses, uncertain what his next move should be. He hears the barest crackling of twigs. Something is moving stealthily, just metres away.

Bowvayne creeps oh so slowly from trunk to trunk.

82

Now the sound is a drawn-out, throaty rattle. Dangerous and deliberate. He peers round a tree to see what is there. And finds he's staring straight into the amber eyes of the biggest black panther he's ever seen!

Six

The big cat is nearly two metres long, with a long tail and sleek, jet-black fur from the top of its ears to the tip of its tail. It is hard to say which of them is more surprised to see the other, the man or the beast. But the black panther reacts quickest. With a roar.

There is a whirring of wings as a flock of ibis make hurriedly for the sky. The roar of the big cat at such close quarters is a quite terrifying experience. Almost eardrum-splitting in loudness. The sound seems to shake the earth and the leaves in the trees. Certainly Bowvayne is shaking like a leaf.

A closely packed clump of trees behind it means that the big cat is unable to retreat. Its only means of escape (*or attack*) is in Bowvayne's direction. All of a sudden the panther springs. It does a sort of vertical twist in the air and aims a swipe at the hapless adventurer, its claws unsheathed.

Terrified, Bowvayne stumbles backwards. He feels mur-derously sharp claws graze his right shoulder. In another instant the black panther has bounded away at an amazing speed, to disappear among the trees.

Bowvayne stays lying on the ground for a considerable period of time: he is clearly in a state of shock. He finally regains his nerve and his composure. Slowly he makes his way back to camp.

An ashen-faced Strange greets him. 'I've had a terrible time, mate. I couldn't find mixed bean salad anywhere.'

Bowvayne tells his partner about his encounter in a shrill, hysterical tone, all the while waving his arms about. While this is going on, the more practical Mythbuster is preparing a salad dinner. When Bowvayne has finished his tale, Strange says, 'Now where did I put my spice rack?'

'What are we having for dinner?' Bowvayne asks, giving up and taking an interest in more mundane affairs for once. They are both sitting on the ground behind the Mythrover, where there is a little shade.

Strange stops scratching the ant bites on his ankles and gives Bowvayne a cheesy grin. 'Your favourite. Chicken drumsticks.'

'Great!'

'I'll just get them from the tent.' He climbs languidly to his feet. Suddenly he is yelling at the top of his voice and shattering the peaceful, domestic, desert scene. 'Mate! Mate! I've just spotted the panther.' He points behind the Mythtent to the steep bank. 'It's up there! To the Myth-rover. Quick!'

Strange is already pulling away in the car when his fellow Mythbuster scrambles to his feet, throws the door open and leaps into the passenger seat. The vehicle coughs and splutters up the embankment, while Strange adopts his familiar hunched position over the steering wheel, a study in concentration. Nursing the Mythrover up the steep bank, weaving around among the eucalypts, he murmurs, almost to himself, 'Maybe it smelt the chicken drumsticks.'

Once again the light is failing quickly. The ground levels out and the pair see the desert stretching out into the distance. But no big cat.

Bowvayne grabs the camera from the back seat and puts its strap round his neck, ready. 'Let's do one circuit of Bunyip Swamp. We might get lucky.'

'Right.'

Soon the Mythrover is blundering through the undergrowth. It tries to shake itself to pieces as it hits deep ruts in the makeshift track. The darkness is now total.

Bowvayne unwinds the passenger window and there is an inrush of aromatic air and night-time sounds: chirpings and chatterings, hootings and raspings, scrapings and caterwaulings. Plugging a high-powered, 120-watt halogen spotlight into the cigarette lighter fitting, Bowvayne leans out of the window and searches the horizon for the black panther. He is nearly thrown clear out through the window when Strange narrowly avoids a callitris pine in the middle of a sharp bend in the bank. The Mythrover leans alarmingly on the passenger side, the roof-rack scraping against a sand dune. Strange wipes his forehead.

'Steady, mate. We nearly lost it then!' Bowvayne continues to scan the desert with the powerful spotlight. Captured in its beam are dozens of kangaroos and wallabies and a couple of emus; and the light rain-shower that has just begun looks like countless glittering diamonds. And far off, for the last time, they see it again. The black panther.

Rain starts to drum loudly on the roof of the Mythrover.

SEVEN

It's nine o'clock on the following night, and the rain is torrential. It lashes the little two-man tent with the Mythbusters sitting miserably inside.

'There's no choice. We're going to have to get out of here right now,' Strange frets. 'Otherwise we'll be washed away.'

'You don't think the rain'll ease up in a little while?' Bowvayne says hopefully. He doesn't fancy getting soaked through if he doesn't have to.

'No. If we leave it any longer, the Mythrover might get stuck in the mud. Then we'd be in real trouble . . .'

Two depressed and rain-drenched, would-be bunyip-hunters pack up the tent as the downpour continues to lash them. Already there is a film of water across the whole of Bunyip Swamp. Water is pouring down freshly formed channels in the embankment, and the swamp begins to fill at a frightening speed.

Without warning they hear a loud booming roar, like the foghorn of a ghost-ship full of lost souls.

The Mythbusters clutch at each other. 'What . . .?'

'What in God's name was that?'

From another part of the swamp they hear an answering booming noise. This time it's further away. Somewhere out there in the darkness.

'Bunyips?' Bowvayne asks, unsure how many more nasty surprises he can take.

Strange says chillingly, 'Maybe they're out hunting. They might have picked up our scent already.' Hastily he tosses the rest of their equipment into the back of the Mythrover.

The two scared and soggy adventurers squelch into the front, Strange gunning the engine. At first it refuses to start. Then, just as the vehicle chugs into life, there is another sound: a weird 'pop', as if a great cork of solid clay had been unstoppered. The earth trembles, shaking the Mythrover from side to side. There is a great inrushing of water near by, as if filling a sudden vacuum.

The Mythbusters have a momentary vision of a vast black shape lumbering in front of the car, but it is almost totally obscured by the darkness.

Bowvayne unwinds the window and prepares to take a photograph.

'Don't you dare set off the flash,' Strange snaps.

The creature makes a booming roar and fades into the night.

EIGHT

The rainstorm continues unabated. A threatening drum-roll of thunder rumbles across the sky like a gigantic dinosaur suffering from indigestion. The Mythrover's wheels spin wildly and uselessly as it still won't move. All the while the water level in Bunyip Swamp is rising. Bowvayne is impatient, overexcited, perhaps even slightly hysterical. 'Come on, Chris! Get it moving. We need to find out if they really are bunyips!'

A scandalized Strange gives Bowvayne a sour, sidelong glance. 'Are you completely mad? We're about to drown, and you're worried about chasing monsters. Now this is what we'll ...' Lightning flashes so brightly that for a split-second it is as if night has been transformed into day, and the effect shocks Strange into silence. But he keeps revving the engine, while the tyres carve out ever deeper graves for themselves in the sodden clay.

Bowvayne swings the passenger door open. 'I've got an idea!' he yells above the pounding rhythm of the rain; he scrambles up a bank, dashes beneath the protective umbrella of the tall eucalypts, and hunts about until he finds what he's looking for. Clutching two large eucalyptus branches and a pile of brushwood, he races back to the Mythrover. Wedging it all against the base of the front tyres, he shouts to Strange, 'Now, go!' The vehicle lumbers over the branches and skates forward like a beginner on an ice-rink. Bowvayne leaps back inside the car, dripping wet.

A ferocious bolt of lightning flares in front of the Mythbusters, seeming to grow instant crackling branches that fracture the whole sky. Around them, weird silhouettes suddenly loom, advance, disappear, and then reappear again. Oddly disembodied shadows play in the light of the Mythrover's headlamps, accentuated by each lightning flash. Are they black panthers? Bunyips? Some other secret creatures of the night? It is impossible to say.

The Mythrover trundles up the embankment and out into the unknown. Strange wishes he was in a comfortable armchair at home right now, with his bulldog, Nero, curled comfortably round his ankles, reading his favourite book on home-made jams and preserves. (Strange doing the reading, not Nero!)

As the Mythrover skids about at the top of a particularly treacherous rise, they realize that it has 'bogged down' again. Glumly Bowvayne exits the vehicle and pushes against the back of it with all his might. Strange jams the accelerator to the floor, the engine makes an agonizing scream, and its back tyres throw out mud which finds its way unerringly into Bowvayne's face. He's about to curse when, without warning, the Mythrover jolts forward.

The sudden movement causes Bowvayne to lose his footing, and he slides down the slippery slope, plunging into the raging torrent. He thrashes about, coughing and spluttering, trying to swim back to the bank. The current pulls him under, and the water sings in his ears. All around him in the water are dark, wriggling shapes ... Snakes! Dozens of snakes!

Something drags him out of the torrent by the collar of his shirt. His limbs are still flailing pathetically in mid-air when he sees it's Strange who is ruining the shape of his Mythbusters T-shirt. Strange is practically babbling at his drowned rat of a companion. 'Come on, let's get out of here. Another five minutes and the Mythrover will be underwater!' The rain comes down like great iron stair-rods, pelting them both painfully.

The pair dash to the car, now in a deadly race with the rainstorm to escape the desert. If they win, they'll have a great story to tell. If they lose, they'll drown. Soon the water is gushing around the bottom of the door-frames. 'Another few centimetres of water will stop the engine,' Strange says grimly. On and on they drive. The night seems endless.

Then, at last, a wonderful sight: a man-made road ahead. The edge of the desert. With terrifying sudden-ness lightning strikes a tree very close to them, and it comes crashing down, barely a metre behind the Mythrover.

And in the distance, right in the heart of the Little Desert, an almost indiscernible sound comes out of the chaos all round them: a final booming roar. The adventurers reach the tarmac road. The desert has kept some of its secrets, so it decides to let them go. This time.

Artist's impression of bunyip and big cat

CASE CLOSING NOTES

The Mythbusters can categorically state that there are big cats in the Little Desert.

Large and dangerous animals lurking in places where they aren't meant to be found is one of those peculiar types of mystery that seem to capture the popular imagination. In Britain the dreaded Beast of Exmoor is an obvious example – 'the beast that screamed in the night, displayed supernatural cunning in eluding its enemy, and was blamed for the deaths of nearly 100 sheep and lambs', according to expert in the unknown, Arthur C. Clarke.

But, in practical terms, *how* do these animals and, in our case, these big cats end up where they shouldn't be? Subsequent research by the Mythbusters after their exciting adventures revealed an interesting fact. During the Second World War there was an American military base in the Wimmera region. There were rumours that they kept black panthers (and, some said, pumas as well) as mascots.

When the war ended and it was time for the soldiers to return home, rather than kill their mascots they let them loose in the wild.

However, in the case of Australia's most famous mystery beast, the bunyip is not so readily explained. A fascinating *Fortean Times* magazine (No. 76) article, entitled 'Just What Is A Bunyip Anyway?' said that for sightings, 'The bunyip's heyday was from the 1840s to 1900'. It also stated that 'The Aborigines of south-eastern Australia appear to have believed in two different types of bunyip . . . Both were reported from the same areas, but the local Aborigines were virtually annihilated so there is less information on the subject than we'd like. Whites saw some things though . . . The latest bunyip sightings were in the 1970s . . .'

So what did the Mythbusters see lumbering in front of the car that night, perhaps three metres tall and making a loud booming roar? It's certainly not in any of the well-thumbed books on Australian fauna in the Mythbusters' archives. It may have been a bunyip. But it remains a mystery – for now.

4. The Roc

MYTHBUSTERS CASE FILE

TITLE:	The Roc
CODE:	001Mal/Sey 220292
LOCATION:	The Maldives – 2,000 tiny coral islands scattered across the Indian Ocean. The Seychelles, 86 islands further south, generally larger and more mountainous, with tangled forests
MYTHBUSTERS:	Bowvayne Chris Strange
TERRAIN:	Sandy islands with swaying coconut palms. Sparkling lagoons. Coral reefs. Some forest
DIFFICULTIES:	Occasional high humidity. Occasional sharks, barracudas, moray eels. Constant threat of succumbing to the island

paradise, lying in the sun with a cocktail and never wanting to get up again

MISSION: Full-scale investigation. To attempt to photograph the giant bird from Arabian mythology

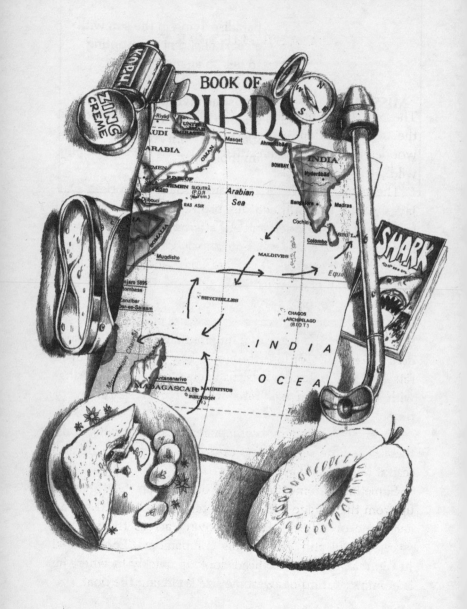

CASE HISTORY

The reflected sunlight glitters diamonds and sapphires in the translucent blue waters of the Indian Ocean. A long wooden fishing-boat skims over the water, the sail flapping wildly from its tall mast.

The group of five Sri Lankans aboard comprises Dav Jayasundera, his girlfriend, his brother, the brother's girlfriend and a female servant. All afternoon they have been fishing for shark and chasing shoals of skipjack tuna — without much success. They are somewhere in the Maldives, the waters of which make up more than 99 per cent of the whole country's area.

Sharp dorsal fins are seen cutting through the sea towards them: the scene of a hundred nightmares. Jayasundera's brother, Gordon, throws a bag of bloodied dead rats into the water. A local fisherman has told them that with this bait you will catch whitetip reef sharks every time.

As the Jayasundera brothers ready their fishing-rods, they all see the serried rows of dagger-sharp teeth rip and tear at the bait and at each other.

Something momentarily blots out the sun. Dav glances up from the savage scene before him, expecting to see an aeroplane or a flock of birds moving across the sky. He swears aloud and yells to his companions, 'Look! Look! Just look up there!' Four heads look up quickly to where he is pointing. A bird of awesome size is circling the boat.

'It is roc,' says the frightened servant-girl.

It senses that there is prey in the sea and wheels about for a moment longer. Then it swoops downwards, an immense black blur with talons.

Is it one of them or a shark that will be its food? With screams of terror they all fling themselves on to the deck. Dav feels a rush of air just above him as the great bird passes overhead. There is a horrifying screech.

The roc rises from the water with a shark in its talons. It flies off in the direction from which it has come, fading at last from their vision.

The world of Arabian mythology is fabulous and fanciful: full of cruel kings and gentle genies: magnificent medieval palaces and dark dungeons; and heroes such as Aladdin, Ali Baba and Sinbad the Sailor. Also featuring strongly among this rich vein of myth and legend are the 'Great Birds': the griffins of the Caucasus, the phoenix of Arabia, the simurgs of Persia and the giant rocs of the Indian Ocean.

According to the famous Venetian explorer, Marco Polo (1254–1324), the roc inhabits Madagascar and other nearby islands off the east coast of Africa. He relates that ' . . . the envoy . . . brought the Great Kaan one of its wing-feathers. And I, Marco Polo, measured it and I found it to be 90 of my spans in length; and the compass of the quill end was twice my palm; truly it was a marvellous sight to see . . . They say, then, that it is so big and so strong that it can take up an elephant in its talons . . .' It is shaped like an eagle but is so huge that each feather is as large as a palm leaf.

The size and strength of the roc are legendary; many

tales of encounters with the bird exist, particularly in the collection of Arabian tales, *The Thousand and One Nights*. Sightings have persisted to the present day. The Mythbusters had to investigate.

ONE

The Mythbusters had arrived for the adventure of a lifetime. They are 640 kilometres south-west of Sri Lanka, in the Maldives, comprising over 2,000 coral islands, scattered across the crystal waters of the Indian Ocean. It is a true paradise. Bliss. Nirvana. That is, if you like sunburn, salty water stinging your eyes and sand in your mixed bean salad.

'This is paradise,' says Bowvayne.

'Yeah, but, mate,' Chris Strange whinges, 'there's sand in my mixed bean salad.'

Both are sitting on the beach in swimming trunks. Bowvayne gazes across the gleaming white expanse . . .

'You really need a suntan, Chris.'

. . . then over the gleaming white beach to where the coconut palms gently nod over a clear blue lagoon. The island is so tiny it takes only five minutes to walk round it.

Strange applies white zinc cream to his reddening nose. 'Fancy doing some more snorkelling later on?'

Bowvayne remembers the amazing kaleidoscopic beauty of the coral reef they had seen that morning. 'Yeah! Great! I'm hoping we might even catch a glimpse of the famous whale shark. Someone told me they're nearly fifty feet long!'

Strange looks sweaty and nervous. 'A few sea-squirts and a shoal of those pink things with polka dots will suit me fine.'

Scurrying down the beach from the hotel is Tim, the Sri Lankan receptionist (and part-time pedlar of cowrie shells for exorbitant prices).

'Hide your money,' Bowvayne sighs. 'He's not still trying to sell you that cowrie shell convertible nail-file and egg-timer, is he?'

'No, no. I bought a cowrie shell wallet from him yesterday.'

The dark, skinny boy struggles across the sand to them, a half-eaten, suspicious-smelling poppadam waving around in one hand, a cordless phone in the other.

'Looks like your take-away's arrived, Bow!'

Tim is breathless when he reaches the Mythbusters, probably from the weight of dozens of cowrie-shell necklaces round his neck, all with price-tags on them. 'Telephone, sahs! Telephone!' he jabbers excitedly.

'Thank you, Tim,' says Strange, taking the phone and tipping him. 'Hello? ... Ah, thanks for calling, Dav ... Where are you? ... Malé ... You think you might have spotted this bird again! ... Definitely remember the location? ... Breadfruit curry ... We'll be there ...' He hands the phone back to the Sri Lankan.

Bowvayne's face is an enormous grin. 'It's the roc again, isn't it?'

'Yeah, he thinks he's seen it again,' Strange replies. He clambers to his feet and rolls up his Daffy Duck beach towel. 'Come on. Let's go. Dav is in Malé right now.' He struggles to keep his voice even, but his innards are churning with excitement. 'If Dav isn't exaggerating, they've all seen easily the biggest bird in the world!'

Two

The Mythbusters dash down the beach and push their narrow, coconut-palm fisherman's boat over the bleached white sand and into the sea. Its outboard motor coughs into life as Strange pulls the cord, and they head out into the ocean.

They're on the equator and the midday sun is merciless. Sweat pours from every pore.

'Better put on shirts, or we'll get a bad burn,' says Strange. They both pull on white Mythbusters T-shirts (available from good clothes stores everywhere).

Bowvayne checks his map and compass. 'I reckon it's about a three-hour chug to Malé.'

The journey from their resort to the Maldivian capital is a magical one. A school of dolphins escorts them out of the lagoon. They chatter amiably to the Mythbusters while riding in the boat's bow wave. One leaps out of the water as it swims, another performs a playful somersault. Bowvayne has an overwhelming desire to become one of them.

On the seaward side of the lagoon, hawksbill turtles glide gracefully beneath the wooden boat. All around them the great Indian Ocean breaks upon the sandy shores of the tiny tropical islands, the white horses running up to the coconut palms and bougainvillaea bushes, where multi-coloured parakeets squawk and squabble.

Late afternoon. Bowvayne and Strange tie the boat up at the pier in Malé. Although this is the capital, it is little more than a couple of square kilometres in area. The tiny town is composed of coral-stone houses and, looming in the distance, is the huge, three-storey Islamic Centre, where a library, conference hall and classrooms are housed beneath its 133 minarets.

The pair walk through the sandy streets to the Mijheed-hee Magu, the area where the cafés are to be found. The whole place stinks of fish and coconut oil. A little, wrinkled man ambles past them with an enormous, smiling fish hanging over his shoulders. An old crone in a cotton dress is slouched in a shady alleyway, smoking a hookah pipe.

They finally find the shopfront sign they are looking for; it is a seedy-looking eating-house with tables and chairs outside. A bedraggled grey parrot in a rusted cage greets them by swearing at Strange in Divehi, the local language.

'I think he likes you,' Bowvayne says, smiling at his partner.

Strange is impatient. 'Do you realize how many thousand miles we've come for this? The amount of red ink I'll have to use on the end-of-the-month Mythbuster Accounts if this is a wasted trip!'

'Oh, don't worry about all that,' Bowvayne replies airily. He lives his life like a monkey who thinks the world is an enormous banana tree – and never sees the skins on the ground.

Strange reflects on the telephone call that brought them here. The week before, their old schoolfriend, Dav Jayasundera, had phoned Mythbase (Oz)-1 from Malé with a quite incredible tale. While out on a fishing-boat he and a group of friends had been attacked by an enormous bird of prey. Its size and description, added to the fact that the incident occurred in the Indian Ocean, all hinted at something fantastic: that this was the roc of Arabian mythology. This was a case too good to miss, he suggested, and the Mythbusters should come and meet him in Malé as soon as they could. Bowvayne and Strange set out immediately, leaving Ian Digweed behind in Australia to continue research on the UFOs of the Nullarbor Plain.

Bowvayne's stomach-radar is searching without success for a plate of chicken drumsticks. 'Let's sit down, Chris, I'm starving.'

'I'm going to have the breadfruit curry,' Strange says decisively.

They sit at a table. Bowvayne reads the menu, written exclusively in a foreign script — that is, foreign to them. When a scruffy old waiter with stained teeth shuffles up, pen and notepad in hand ready to take their order, Bowvayne points vaguely at something about half-way down the list. 'That's the breadfruit curry, I'm sure of it,' he says confidently. 'I'm going to have it too.'

'Is it the breadfruit curry?' Strange asks the waiter. The fellow just nods happily.

As soon as they've ordered, they hear a familiar booming laugh and look round. It is their Sri Lankan friend, Dav Jayasundera. He strides up to their table, right hand outstretched and booming laugh replaced by a booming voice. 'It's great to see you both.'

Handshakes and greetings over, Jayasundera takes a seat, then summons the waiter, making an order in fluent Divehi. The Mythbusters listen jealously.

'Could you get us something to drink, Dav?' Bowvayne asks.

'Sure.' Then to the waiter: 'Kiru sarbat.'

His skin the colour of hazel-nuts, he is a tall, powerfully

built man in his mid-twenties – a far cry from his childhood when he had the physique of a stick insect on hunger strike. His eyes are very dark and calculating, yet there is also a hint of warmth in them. His black hair, like a raven's wing, frames a handsome face. He wears one of his infamous batik shirts, a vulgar clash of purple and yellow.

Even before they have finished with 'small talk', the Maldivian is standing beside them with a heavily laden tray.

Strange looks expectant. 'I'm really looking forward to my breadfruit curry.'

A glass of *kiru sarbat* is placed in front of each of them. Bowvayne take a sip. It has a sweet, milky flavour.

Then the three plates of food are presented. Jayasundera sucks air between his teeth and slouches back in his chair. 'Ah, their *bambukeylu hiti* is wonderful,' he declares, looking down at his plate.

'But you've got the breadfruit curry!' Strange says accusingly, glowering at his own plateful of fish and herbs.

'Yes, I know,' Jayasundera replies. 'That's what *bambukeylu hiti* means: "breadfruit curry".'

The waiter is grinning pathetically at Strange, like a dog waiting for a pat on the head. The Mythbuster forces a smile through clenched teeth.

Strange looks at Bowvayne's plate. He has the same dish: fish with herbs. 'Do you want to swap, Dav?'

The seasoned vindaloo curry-eater thinks for a moment, then: 'No thanks. Too hot for me.'

Bowvayne and Strange both take a mouthful of fish, probably sailfish.

Strange is grumpy. 'What do you mean, "too hot"? It's

lukewarm. And if you mean the other kind of hot, it's quite bland.'

'Yes,' Bowvayne agrees. 'Quite bla ... bla ... bla ... bla ... dy hell!' he finishes, fanning his mouth with his hands.

'Man the pumps! Send for the fire brigade! My mouth's on fire!' Strange gasps. The pair drain their drinks, their eyes, mouths, noses and ears streaming from the vicious spice.

'That is called *githeyo mirus*,' Jayasundera manages to say between booms of laughter. 'Some say it is too hot for the Devil himself!'

Bowvayne wheezes in reply. Strange fizzles like a dying firecracker.

Later on, after the Mythbusters' dinner-time perform-ance, Strange has regained some of his dignity. 'Give us an exact description of what you saw,' he says, taking a mini-recorder from the breast-pocket of his shirt.

After retelling the amazing events of the week before, when the giant bird had swooped down and plucked a shark from the sea, Jayasundera looks at the Mythbusters and shakes his head. 'As you know, I'm not interested in myths and mysteries like you are ... but this ... this was something else.' He picks up his glass and swallows the *kiru sarbat* in one gulp.

'Could you show us *exactly* where it happened?' Bowvayne asks, his eyes shining with the fanatical gleam that normally means trouble for everyone.

'Sure.'

'Right now?'

The big Sri Lankan is doubtful. 'It'll be dark before we get there ...'

'Yeah, mate. He's right ...' Strange begins.

106

But Bowvayne's mind is made up. 'We don't need to worry about little things like that! Let's go!'

THREE

Early evening, back at the boat. The trio strap themselves into life-jackets and are soon chugging steadily away from Malé. They can almost taste the salt in the air.

Bowvayne has that face-consuming grin on again and is gabbling breathlessly. 'Ihopeyou'rereadyforthisI'vegota feelingthisisgoingtobethebigonethebiggestbirdintheworld . . . wow!'

Jayasundera wonders how he got himself talked into this.

But Strange is not impressed. 'Even if the roc loops the loop for us, it's going to be too dark to see anything, let alone take photographs.' As if to prove his point, the sun promptly sinks below the horizon. The sky is shot with soft hues of gold, a breathtakingly beautiful scene, filled with the silhouettes of seabirds on the wing.

The boat circles the area where the Sri Lankan thinks he saw the roc. It has taken almost five hours to reach this spot. They are now in complete darkness, although it is still pleasantly warm. Only their torches' powerful beams offer any hint of what is 'out there'.

'I'll drop anchor so we can listen out for a while,' says Jayasundera.

Another hour passes. All they hear is the steady slap-slap of water rocking the boat from side to side. Jayasundera feels the first nauseous bubblings of sea-sickness from within.

Unaware of their friend's suffering, the Mythbusters are

concluding another argument. Bowvayne is thoughtful. 'Where would a roc go to at night? The nearest island, perhaps?'

Strange nods. 'That'd be a pretty good guess. It's more likely to be somewhere like that than out here.'

Bowvayne's mind clutches at straws. 'Are there any islands near by, Dav?'

'There's one less than ten minutes away, as it happens,' Jayasundera replies with a casual air that conceals a wave of relief surging through him. He would have done or said anything to get his feet on dry land again, even if it had been infested with tigers. 'I'll take you there now.'

Twenty-five paces from the island, Jayasundera leaps from the boat and swims ashore. He races up the sand and disappears into the darkness.

Bowvayne and Strange look at one another in bafflement.

'He's really going overboard with enthusiasm, isn't he?' Strange quips.

'Yeah. There could have been sharks or anything in there. I thought I was the only one who did crazy things like that!'

The Mythbusters guide the boat up on to the beach and then drag it inland as far as they can. They scramble up the talcum-powder-like sand and move cautiously into the deep gloom of the closely packed coconut palms, all the while trying to shout as quietly as possible, 'Dav! Dav! Where are you?'

Finally he reappears. 'Sorry about that, guys. I felt a bit ill,' he mumbles, embarrassed.

'You going to be OK?' Strange asks, concerned.

'Sure,' says Jayasundera. He trips over a fallen tree and lands heavily. 'Sure.'

The trio advance, torches scanning for danger. A flock of startled birds explodes from the trees with a snap-snap-snap of beating wings. The heroes all jump.

'If we're frightened by crows, God knows what we're going to do when we find the roc,' Jayasundera says without humour.

There is the sound of a heavy thump behind them. They grip one another tightly. 'The roc?' Strange's voice is hoarse, panicky.

'No. A falling coconut.' They move on.

'Have you ever had the feeling that you're being watched?' Bowvayne mumbles, swinging his torch upwards.

'Yeah, right now,' Strange whispers back. His torch beam catches a massive black silhouette. The mysterious creature crashes to the ground some distance away.

'That's it. I'm getting out of here, with or without you,' Strange says in a low voice. This decision is final. He will not be swayed under any circumstances.

'I'm with you, Chris,' Jayasundera hisses.

Too late.

The dark shape leaps at them with a screech that shrivels the hair from the back of their necks. In the split-second that it is illuminated by their torches, the three of them see what looks like a hairy ape dressed in rags. Dark, blazing eyes. A sharp and deadly weapon glittering . . .

Someone yells the Mythbusters' motto: 'Run away!' They gallop away with all the dignity of chickens fleeing a fox in their coop, stopping only to push the boat out to sea.

FOUR

The trio are slumped, exhausted, in the boat as it heads back to the sanctuary of their hotels.

Bowvayne is disgusted. 'Who said "run away"? That might've been the photograph of a lifetime.'

'The end of your lifetime, you mean,' Jayasundera says seriously.

'I noticed you'd overtaken me by the time we got to the boat,' Strange points out to Bowvayne.

An unrepentant Bowvayne says, 'I just got caught up in the hysteria of the moment. Anyway, what do you think it was, back there?'

'I know what it wasn't,' Jayasundera drawls wearily. 'A roc.'

'Maybe it was Robinson Crusoe,' Strange teases. He is almost his old self again (minus the back-of-the-neck hair).

Bowvayne takes seriously the suggestion that it could have been someone marooned. 'If the name of that place is Treasure Island, then we just met Ben Gunn!'

'I've just realized something,' Jayasundera booms, fear coming into his eyes. 'Convicted criminals in the Maldives are set down on uninhabited islands for the length of their sentence. We've probably just run slap-bang into a dangerous prisoner!'

Strange isn't convinced. 'Surely they'd have better security around the place than that?'

'It sounds too cushy to me.' Bowvayne is also doubtful. He adds with a grin, 'Hey, it'd be pretty ironic if you're right, though. Tourists paying thousands of pounds to get the same treatment as Maldivian convicts!'

They all laugh.

'All the same,' the Sri Lankan says finally, 'I vote we steer clear of that island from now on. That was one hell of a dagger he had on him.'

After returning Jayasundera to Malé, the Mythbusters arrive back at the resort hotel, collapsing into their beds just before eight in the morning.

Noon. A rumpled Bowvayne pads softly from the hotel room, careful not to wake Strange, who is snoring like a hibernating grizzly bear. He walks tiredly across the sandy courtyard to the optimistically named Business Centre, basically a broom cupboard housing a fax-machine and a telephone.

Digweed has faxed through some information about the Biggest Birds, Living and Extinct, which he'd found in *The Guinness Book of Records*. Bowvayne and Strange had left for the Maldives in such a hurry that their normally extensive library research had had to be skipped. Strange hadn't been pleased with the situation. 'I think it's sloppy to start a new case without thorough research.' Bowvayne just pretended he hadn't been pleased with the situation.

He sits in the only chair in the place, a rickety affair, and settles down to read. The heaviest bird in the world is the Andean condor, weighing in at around 10–14 kilos. The wandering albatross definitely has the largest wing-span, with some reports of measurements up to 4 metres. And the extinct giant teratorn that lived in Argentina around six million years ago is another fascinating bird.

111

Fossil remains discovered near Buenos Aires suggest this vulture had a wingspan of 7–7.5 metres.

At the bottom of the faxed page, in Digweed's untidy handwriting, it says, 'According to the famous Venetian explorer, Marco Polo [still 1254–1324], the roc inhabits Madagascar and other islands off the east coast of Africa."

Bowvayne exhales heavily. 'Wow! Dav's bird was bigger than any of these. Well done, Diggers!' He races up the steps to the hotel room and flings the door open, yelling, 'Chris! We're going to Madagascar!'

Strange groans, pulls his bedspread over his head and continues snoring. In his sleep he mumbles, 'More red ink. More red ink . . .'

FIVE

The Mythbusters walk from their hotel room down to the beach – a Maldivian beach, not a Madagascan one. It is three weeks after their midnight jaunt.

They scan the horizon. No sign of Dav. Just a twenty-metre luxury yacht and a kid windsurfing.

Strange doesn't like surprises. 'I wonder what Dav meant when he said he'd borrow an old piece of junk from a friend of his uncle's? I'm not sailing in something unsafe.'

Bowvayne has finally got his own way. An investigation spanning the whole Indian Ocean. 'Don't worry, Chris,' he says soothingly. 'When he said "junk" he probably meant as in the Chinese, flat-bottomed variety.'

They put their belongings near the water's edge and sit on suitcases.

Strange is still stubborn. 'It's going to be some floating Rent-A-Wreck; I can feel it in my water . . .'

'Hey! You guys!' Jayasundera shouts from the twenty-metre luxury yacht. 'Are you coming aboard or what?'

Strange warms instantly. 'Remind me to get my water changed when we get home,' he says to Bowvayne.

The pair wade to the yacht with suitcases, fishing rods, scuba gear, binoculars, cameras, compasses, maps, a bag of bloodied dead rats and three rounds of sailfish sandwiches. Jayasundera hauls the Mythbusters and their gear over the silver guard-rail and on to the polished wooden deck.

The interior of the yacht is awesome in its opulence: an air-conditioned cabin and bathroom each, in the finest dark mahogany wood. Also aboard are Jayasundera's Uncle Lalith, an expert sailor, and Adolf the German chef. Even as Bowvayne and Strange bumble round the boat, open-mouthed with amazement, Adolf is in the customized kitchen preparing lobster salads.

After unpacking their suitcases and changing into dry shorts, the pair meet back at the yacht's bar. Bowvayne acts as barman and makes them an ice-cool drink each.

'Shall we make everyone walk the plank and steal the boat?' Bowvayne says, only half joking.

'All right. Oh, except Adolf,' Strange replies, remembering his all-important stomach.

Jayasundera comes down the steps leading below deck and joins them. 'I've got those maps you asked for, Bow,' he says, handing them over. Bowvayne spreads the largest one out across the bar-top. Jayasundera pulls up a stool and joins them.

The excited Mythbuster runs a trembling finger down the map. 'So this is it. Next stop the Seychelles. Then on to the Comores. Circumnavigate Madagascar. A quick stop in Mauritius. Return the boat to Colombo, Sri Lanka. We're sure to find the roc and half a dozen other things in that time and . . .'

Strange interrupts, attempting to bring his madcap friend back to the real world. 'It could take months!'

There's that fanatical gleam in Bowvayne's eyes again. 'Yeah. It's great, isn't it?'

But Strange attempts to reason with Jayasundera. 'Surely we've only got the boat for a few days at most?'

'Oh, no,' Jayasundera says blithely. 'We've got it for as long as we want. Uncle Lalith's friend has got a couple more yachts like this!'

Strange looks astounded. He feels surrounded by lunatics. Wonderful, irresponsible lunatics. If you can't beat them join them, he thinks.

After a magnificent lobster each for lunch, eaten sitting up on deck, Bowvayne asks the Sri Lankans, 'When are we leaving?'

'It is not so simple,' the portly Lalith replies, sipping a glass of chilled white wine. He is in his late fifties, small and grey-haired, but there is immense dignity in his demeanour. 'A hundred subtleties of wind direction and water current have to be considered . . .'

Tim, the hotel receptionist, makes a bee-line for them down the beach, brandishing his range of expensive and completely useless cowrie shell souvenirs.

'. . . And we're leaving right this second,' says the old sailor. He lurches to his feet and winds in the anchor frantically.

Before long the yacht is cruising steadily south, past hundreds of coral reefs and tiny, uninhabited islands.

Further down the Indian Ocean than the Mythbusters have ever been before.

SIX

Somewhere along the chain of low coral atolls between the Maldives and the Seychelles, the luxury yacht has dropped anchor. It is six days later. Dav, Lalith and Adolf are fishing for their lunch. Bowvayne and Strange are about to go snorkelling.

The Mythbusters are about to jump overboard when Strange remembers something. 'Adolf, do you know how to make breadfruit curry?'

'Vot iss das?' the chef asks apologetically.

Strange starts playing charades with the hapless German. First he mimes 'bread'.

'And this is a piece of fruit falling into water,' Bowvayne says, giving his friend a tremendous push overboard.

The pair swim around the reef, among the astonishing variety and number of colourful underwater creatures. The yellow-and-blue clown fish reclining in the toxic tentacles of sea-anemones. Wrass, goby, damselfish, butterflyfish, triggerfish, surgeonfish, lionfish, goatfish, cowfish, unicorn-fish. Vast shoals like a dazzling dream before their eyes.

Parrotfish loudly crunching the hard coral in their power-ful jaws. A majestic manta ray gliding overhead like an extra-terrestrial on some timeless journey among the stars. A moray eel lurking in a crack in the coral. Warily, the two humans pass them by.

There is a sudden flurry of activity all along the reef. Fish are darting in all directions. Large, dark phantom-silhouettes loom just above the Mythbusters. A dead rat drifts down between them, down to the ocean floor.

Bowvayne is appalled. Someone incredibly stupid has become impatient at 'hooking' nothing for lunch and has thrown in the shark bait. He sees Strange rolling his eyes in disgust. The pair realize that those phantom-silhouettes are sharks. Hammerhead sharks.

Bowvayne's mind, nearly unhinged with fear, treats him to the spectacle of being torn apart in an orgy of gore and maiming by those sharks, so he follows Strange as he dives deeper, thinking he has a plan. There's no way he can do that for long. Without an aqualung, he'll soon have to come up for air a long way from the boat.

Unfortunately, Strange doesn't have a plan. In blind panic he's dived as far from the sharks as possible. An instinctive reaction, completely forgetting he has only a snorkel, and getting a mouthful of saltwater.

Now the Mythbusters need air. They float helplessly upward. The hammerheads move closer. Any second now, they'll move in for the kill, Bowvayne thinks.

They make it to the surface. They're still alive. Both gasp for breath, looking round frantically for the sharks.

'W-where . . .?' Strange stammers.

Bowvayne is puzzled. 'Gone. Some-something frightened them off.'

Thankful at their miraculous escape, they swim back to the boat, 300 metres away. Then they see it: a momentary glimpse of a mighty bird retreating from their vision, a hammerhead shark in its talons. Making for the island on the horizon.

SEVEN

'Quick! Quick!' Strange yells to the crew as he scrambles back on deck.

Bowvayne is right behind him. 'Follow that bird!'

The schooner buzzes with excitement. Lalith steers the sleek white vessel straight for the island ahead. Everyone is taking it in turns to look through the only pair of binoculars handy — even though there's no sign of the bird now.

'I think I saw it,' Jayasundera says hopefully.

'But it could've been anything,' says his uncle.

'Definitely the roc, definitely,' Bowvayne says firmly.

Strange agrees with him. 'Seagulls don't carry off hammerhead sharks!'

All five of them believe that they're sounding calm and rational, but they are, in fact, babbling like children who have caught a glimpse of Santa Claus. Even dour old Adolf is chattering away happily to himself in German.

'Faster!' Bowvayne urges the skipper manically.

Strange bounds down the steps below deck to throw the necessary equipment for the investigation into his backpack.

The yacht is close to the shoreline now. The Mythbusters and Jayasundera leap overboard. The temperature must be well into the nineties, even though evening isn't far away, and the shock of the water right up to their armpits is a pleasant one. They wade through the surf, Strange holding the backpack above his head.

Sixteen hundred kilometres off the east coast of Africa, this beautiful island is perhaps eight kilometres long. Beyond the palm-fringed beach it rises abruptly, the interior becoming mountainous and lush with vegetation.

The trio march up the sandy white beach to the lofty palms.

They clamber up an outcrop of massive, rectangular and square-shaped boulders, the largest over six metres high. It is a difficult climb. They graze their knees and bruise their fingers in tiny crevices. After scaling the rocks, they pause for a moment, taking large swigs from Strange's water-bottle. It is almost unbearably hot up here, at the foot of a shaded forest slope.

'The roc must live up here somewhere. It'd certainly be left undisturbed,' Bowvayne gasps, the thrill of the chase still buoying up his exhausted body.

Jayasundera couldn't agree more. 'Yeah. We're the only ones stupid enough to come all the way up here and annoy it.'

'It might just have flown straight across the top of the island without stopping, you know,' Strange snaps sardonically. 'It may be in Mauritius by now.'

'You don't really think that, do you?' Bowvayne asks, crestfallen.

'Probably not,' Strange answers wearily. He watches the sun dipping into the turquoise ocean, and the yacht bobbing there like a white swan. 'Let's keep going,' he says finally.

They struggle up the steep hillside, the towering taka-maka trees and the casuarinas with their branches like horse-tails soon replaced by thick, moist and shadowy jungle. It is now more humid still. Bowvayne sees a giant land tortoise arch an imaginary eyebrow at him, then lumber with great dignity into the luxuriant undergrowth.

A waterfall tumbles down the hill in front of them. They stop briefly to drink from it and splash each other. Then onward again. Despite the heat, the three of them are still aware of the tropical paradise's splendour: the exotic and colourful flowers, the scent of vanilla from the climbing orchid which gives us the famous flavour, the mango and banana trees, the . . .

'Eureka!' Strange shrieks, almost hysterical with joy. He is a little way ahead of his companions.

Bowvayne and Jayasundera rush to join him. 'It's the roc, isn't it?' Jayasundera hisses, looking around.

'Where is it? Where is it?' Bowvayne demands, his face a sheen of sweat.

'No, no. It's not the roc, it's this,' Strange explains, indicating what he's cradling lovingly in his arms. Nestled like a baby is a large pale fruit he's just plucked from a tree near by. 'Now I'll be able to have my breadfruit curry!'

'You idiot!' Bowvayne replies, disgusted. 'You had us all going there . . .'

Strange is about to justify himself when he catches a slight movement out of the corner of his eye. 'Shhh!'

'What is it?'

Again. 'Shhh!' Something is flapping about just ahead, where there is a small clearing in the jungle.

They take one . . . two steps closer. A glimpse of a powerfully beating underwing, black and white primary feathers at the wingtips.

There is a sound like a wet sponge being dropped on a linoleum floor. Then a harsh cry: 'Aek aek aek aek aek aek.'

Another step forward. They're perhaps twenty paces

from it now. A momentary view of a murderously hooked yellow bill and a head nearly the size of their own. There is a rather eccentric tuft of white feathers above each eye, giving the appearance of pale eyebrows on an all-black face.

This must be the roc they've been searching for. It is tearing skin from an animal of some sort. Strange reaches into his backpack for his camera. Somehow they know that it has sensed them. Activity ceases. Everything goes quiet. The trio begin to circle round the clearing.

Suddenly, from out of the trees, the terrifying sight of vicious talons and a murderous beak blunders towards them.

Bowvayne, Strange and Jayasundera scatter out of its path with their customary expertise.

The roc spreads its wings and launches itself into awkward, ungainly flight. The humans peer out from behind large banana leaves. They see the roc soaring majestically now – the wingspan around six metres – spiralling through the currents above the island.

'I'll never forget this as long as I live,' Bowvayne says emotionally.

Jayasundera is as impressed as the Mythbusters. 'Now I can see why you guys do this sort of thing for a living. That was unbelievable. Just unbelievable.'

Strange is trying in vain to photograph the now tiny dot as it disappears into the distance. 'Damn and blast!' he curses, disappointed. 'Another one that got away!'

'Who cares?' Bowvayne says irrepressibly. 'At least we know it exists.'

'I s'pose you're right,' Strange says, mellowing. 'And at least I didn't damage my breadfruit.'

The other two just groan.

In the jungle clearing they find the hammerhead shark, its stomach bloody and exposed, but otherwise intact. Bowvayne looks at the other two, grinning impishly. 'Anyone want a flake supper?'

As they make their way back down the steep hillside, Jayasundera asks, 'What now?'

Bowvayne has that mad gleam in his eye. 'Isn't the last island where the dodo supposedly exists meant to be around here somewhere?'

'That's a thousand miles south at least,' Strange protests.

'That's what I mean, "around here somewhere". What's a thousand miles among friends . . .'

Artist's impression of the roc

CASE CLOSING NOTES

Arthur C. Clarke once wrote, 'Would you care to guess how many kinds of unknown animals – i.e. creatures that have never been described by science – there still remain on this planet? A hundred? A thousand? The answer may well be in the millions . . .'

At first it would seem unlikely that easily the largest flighted bird on earth could escape detection until now. But consider this: the komodo dragon – the largest reptile on Earth – was only discovered this century, in 1912 in fact.

And it isn't as if the roc has just appeared from nowhere. The first clues to its existence lie in mythology, the seed of many truths.

Around 700 years ago, when Marco Polo returned from the Orient to tell Europeans about the roc, he believed they were real. Admittedly their size and powers were grossly exaggerated, but this often happens when the feats of certain animals are passed down from generation to generation and into folklore.

The specimen the Mythbusters saw that evening may be one of just a few that still live. Sadly, it is an all-too-common trend that the specialized hunters at the top of the food-chain – lions, tigers, leopards, bears, sharks, thylacines, eagles and other birds of prey – are dwindling in numbers for any number of reasons.

These few rocs are living remote and isolated lives in one of the few places that are inaccessible to the marauding waves of mankind: tiny, uninhabited islands, surrounded by the vast ocean. Here they live in near anonymity, with just a few fishermen knowing of the existence of these majestic birds.

One last point, and an optimistic one, too. The bird the Mythbusters saw was partially covered in greyish, fluffy down. Most ornithologists would allow us to make the assumption that this was a sign that our roc was immature. This means that these undiscovered birds are still actually breeding . . . But how big would that make its parents?

Mythbusters can be contacted at:

19 Gerrard Street
London W1V 7LA
England

The Stars and Planets
A Beginner's Guide to Space
Brian Jones

Have you ever looked up at the night sky and wondered just what might be out there?

Why does the moon change shape? What is a comet, or a meteor? And could there really be aliens?

Here is a book full of fascinating facts about the stars and planets, and some of the amazing things that happen out in space. With lots of experiments and useful tips on what to look for, you'll soon become an expert star-gazer!

The Aliens are Coming
Plant Life and the Greenhouse Effect
Phil Gates

Alien plants unleash a reign of terror in the countryside!

This could be a headline of the future, unless you do something to help stop it. The greenhouse effect is warming up the earth so that snowmen could become an endangered species. It also means you may have to eat more ice-cream to keep cool in summer. But worse, it may cause the spread of alien plants which will cause havoc in the countryside and could cause some native plants, which like a cool moist climate, to become extinct.

Find out for yourself, through the experiments and information in this original and entertaining book, just what is happening now and what is likely to happen in the future.

Become a scientist and help warn the world about the dangers ahead!

The *Early Times*
Book of Unsolved Mysteries

Is there a monster lurking in the depths of Loch Ness?

Do poltergeists exist?

Did someone else write Shakespeare's plays?

What really happened on board the *Mary Celeste*?

Here are fifty real-life mysteries covering a whole range of topics – grisly unsolved crimes, spontaneous human combustion, curious disappearances and reappearances, big-footed monsters, and strange objects that fall from the sky, to name just a few! Some you may recognize, like the riddle of the Bermuda Triangle and the true identity of Anastasia, while others you may not, like the puzzling story of coffins that moved by themselves. Written in a lively style, each entry gives the latest research as well as past and current thinking.

After reading about these fascinating events you're sure to agree that the world really is a most mysterious place!

50 Questions Your Dog Would Ask the Vet If Your Dog Could Talk

Bruce Fogle

Why do I sometimes feel the urge to bite people's ankles just when they're about to leave the room?

What forms of discipline might people use to train me and how can I best resist?

Why do I dribble whenever I get in a car?

Sometimes my nose is wet; at other times it is dry. Does it matter?

Have you ever wondered what dogs really think about? What their hopes and fears could be and what questions they might like answered? This book will help you understand the view from the floor and let you in on a few tips to improve the life of your four-legged friend.

Now at last, in the comfort of your own home, both dogs and their humans will be amused and amazed by the answers to all those questions your dog has been dying to ask.

The *Early Times*
Behind the Scenes
Switch on, tune in, sit down!
What's really happening behind the scenes to bring you that broadcast, television programme, film or play?

Producers, directors, technicians and many others give their own accounts of what it's like to work in the world of television, film, theatre and radio. Every stage of production is explained in clear and lively detail, from the development of an idea to the final film, performance or recording. It's a fascinating insight into creative ups and downs, problems and solutions and, above all, the team effort required by this demanding industry.

Being one of the audience is much more fun if you know what's happening backstage. Who knows – maybe one day you'll be behind the scenes too!